Brain-Boosting Cryptic Puzzles

Series Editor: Heather Dickson

Puzzle Contributors: Rich Garner, Helen Shute, David King, Colin Russ, Roya Ireland

Additional Contributors: Peter Sorenti, Joel Hilshey

Page Design and Layout: Linley Clode

Cover Design: Gary Inwood Studios

Published by:
LAGOON BOOKS
PO BOX 311, KT2 5QW, UK
PO BOX 990676, Boston, MA 02199, USA

www.lagoongames.com

ISBN: 1902813219

Printed in Singapore

Brain-Boosting Cryptic Puzzles

Introduction

In the same way that physical exercise tones your muscles and makes you fitter, solving puzzles builds up your IQ and hones your intellectual powers.

With this thinking in mind, we have put together a compilaton of fun and challenging puzzles to give you one of the best cerebral workouts ever.

Within this beautifully illustrated book we have brought you 90 of the best cryptic puzzles – that is, puzzles where expectations are thwarted and the solution is never immediately apparent. We have sorted them into chapters.

In **Chapter 1** – you will find the easiest puzzles – ones you should really be able to complete within 60 seconds.

In **Chapter 2** – you will find a slightly more difficult set of puzzles – ones you should complete in two or three minutes.

In **Chapter 3** – you will find a much more difficult range of posers which should take about five minutes to crack.

In **Chapter 4** – you will find the most fiendish puzzles and conundrums that could take up to ten minutes to work out.

Each puzzle has been rated 1 - 3. So as long as you crack each puzzle – within the time limit allocated in each chapter, you can award yourself the points. Helpful scoring cards have been given at the beginning of each chapter to help you keep score. Once you have completed all the chapters, turn to see your overall score on page 191.

For those of you who want to test the theory that practice makes perfect, why not jump to the last chapter of the book and see how you fare? If you solve the puzzle within ten minutes congratulations – you really are a puzzle genius. If you do not, however, then go back to the beginning of the book and do the puzzles in chronological order. This time, when you get to the puzzles in Chapter 4 you should have no excuses – your score should have leapt up after all the practice!

If, by the end of the book, you have still not achieved your ultimate goal and you want more practice, then turn to page 192 to see Lagoon's other Brain-Boosting titles.

Contents

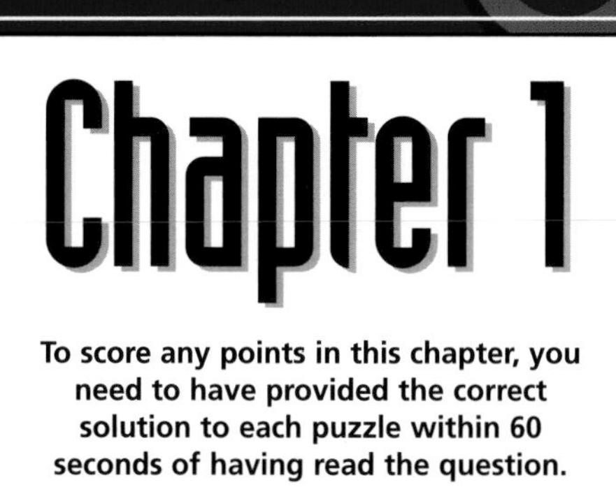

Chapter 1

To score any points in this chapter, you need to have provided the correct solution to each puzzle within 60 seconds of having read the question.

To see individual ratings for each puzzle – see under the title of each question. Once you have completed the chapter, turn to page 8, for help adding up your score.

Then turn to page 53 to start Chapter 2.

Chapter 1 - Scoring

Puzzle points for correct answer

Puzzle	Points	Puzzle	Points
Porky Poser	2	Locker Shocker	2
Brainy Burglar	3	Colour Blind	1
Mystery Sitter	1	Duck Dilemma	1
Name Shuffle	3	Crazy Counting	2
Baby Boom	1	Loyalty Bonus	2
Rook's Revenge	3	First Move	2
Arcane Form	1	Sneaky Cipher	2
Snail Supper	2	Breaking Point	1
Bottle Bargain	2	Family Portrait	3
Car Conundrum	1	Odd One Out	1
Go Forth and Multiply	2	Measuring Madness	2

YOUR TOTAL

/40

Porky Poser

Rating 2 Points

In a farmyard there are several pigs and sows. Each sow can see as many sows as male pigs, but each male pig can see twice as many sows as male pigs. How many pigs (ie male pigs and sows) are there altogether?

Porky Poser - Solution

7 pigs – 3 male pigs and 4 sows.

Brainy Burglar

Rating 3 Points

An old lady has put her life savings in a safe place but she can never remember where it is. To remind herself, she has written the location down in a secret code. While she is out, a thief breaks into the house and finds the coded message. Will he discover the location of the money before the old lady returns?

Brainy Burglar - Solution

A	B	C	D	E	F	G	H	I	J	K	L	M
Z	Y	X	W	V	U	T	S	R	Q	P	O	N

The code is the alphabet written in reverse under the original alphabet.

Mystery Sitter

Rating 1 Point

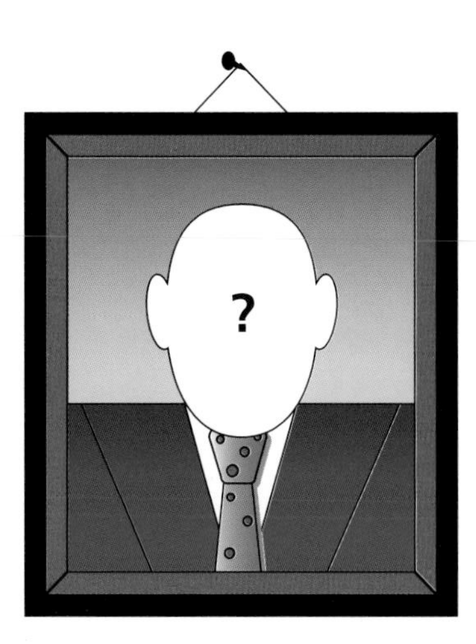

On the wall hung a painting belonging to a particularly reticent person. When asked whom the painting was of, the owner replied, *"I have neither sister nor brother, but my mother's daughter is that man's mother"*. Who was in the painting?

Mystery Sitter – Solution

The owner's son.

Name Shuffle

Rating 3 Points

Don Rowe attempts to rearrange
the letters of his name into one word.
Is this possible?

Name Shuffle - Solution

Yes it is possible to make "one word" from the name Don Rowe.

Baby Boom

Rating 1 Point

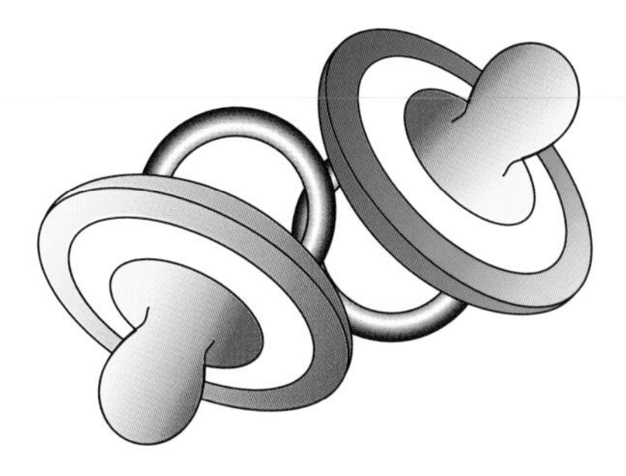

Two girls are born to the same mother on the same day, at the same time, in the same year, and yet, they are not twins? How can this be?

Baby Boom - Solution

They are triplets.

Rook's Revenge

Rating 3 Points

White is moving up the board. White moves first and then mates with his second move. How?

Rook's Revenge - Solution

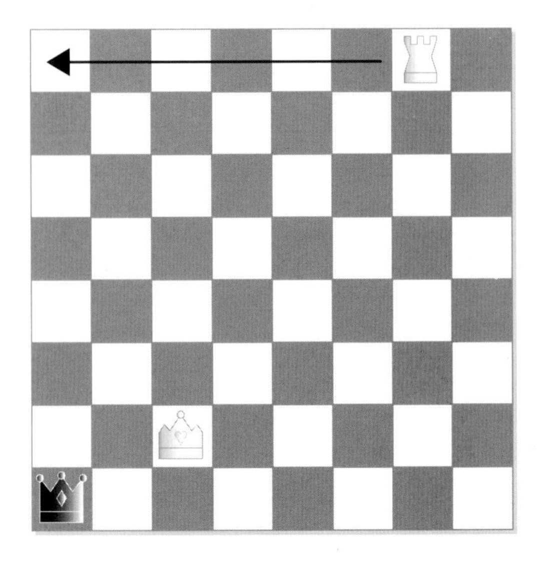

White starts by promoting his pawn to a rook, which will then move horizontally to give mate down the first file (1 Pg8=R Ka2 2 Ra8 mate). White must not promote the pawn to a queen: this would be stalemate!

Arcane Form

Rating 1 Point

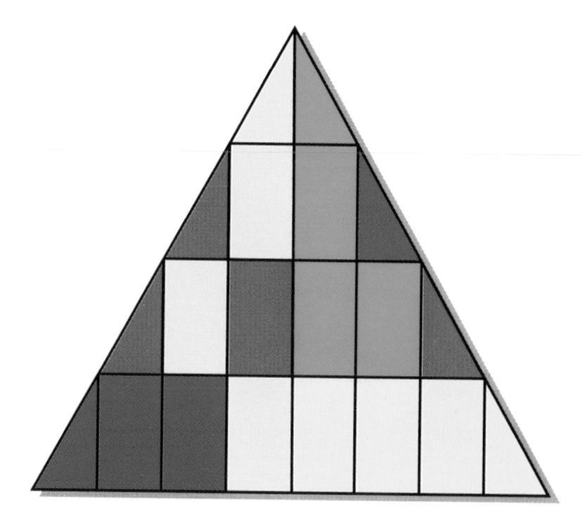

How many triangles can you count?

Arcane Form - Solution

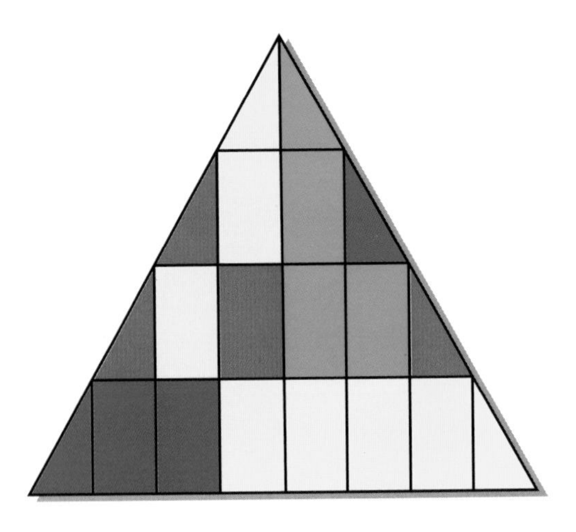

24.

Snail Supper

Rating 2 Points

If six snails can eat 6 shoots in
1/10 of an hour, how many would it take to
eat 100 shoots in 6000 seconds?

Snail Supper - Solution

It would take six snails to eat 100 shoots in 6000 seconds (100 minutes).

Bottle Bargain

Rating 2 Points

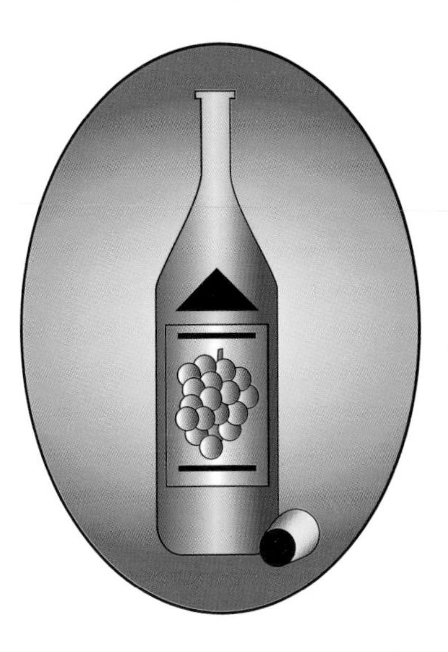

A bottle and a cork cost together $25
and the bottle costs $20 more than the cork.
How much does each cost?

Bottle Bargain - Solution

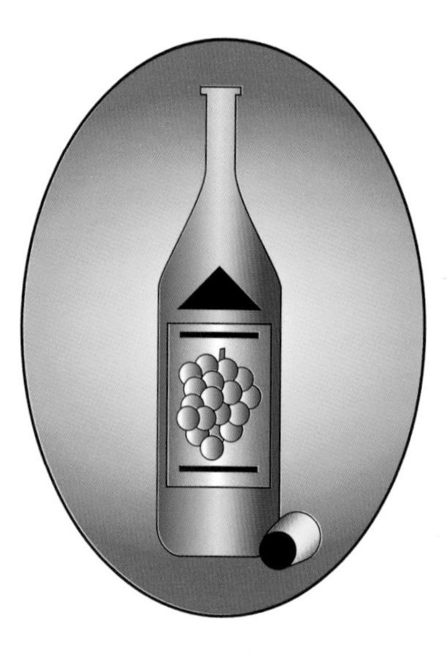

The bottle costs $22.50 and the cork $2.50

Car Conundrum

Rating 1 Point

There are four cars – a red one, a white one, a blue one and a green one. They belong to four friends – John, David, Amy and Mary and are parked next to each other in a street. Amy's car is to the right of the blue car, which is to the right of Mary's. John doesn't like white or blue cars. David's car is not next to John's car and is next to a red car. John and Mary are the only two who have letters in their name which are also in the colours of their car. Who drives which car?

Car Conundrum - Solution

John drives the green one, Mary the red,
David the blue and Amy the white.

Go Forth and Multiply

Rating 2 Points

When a man was asked to describe his children, he said: *"They are all blonds, but two, all redheads, but two, and all brunettes, but two."* How many children did he have?

Go Forth and Multiply - Solution

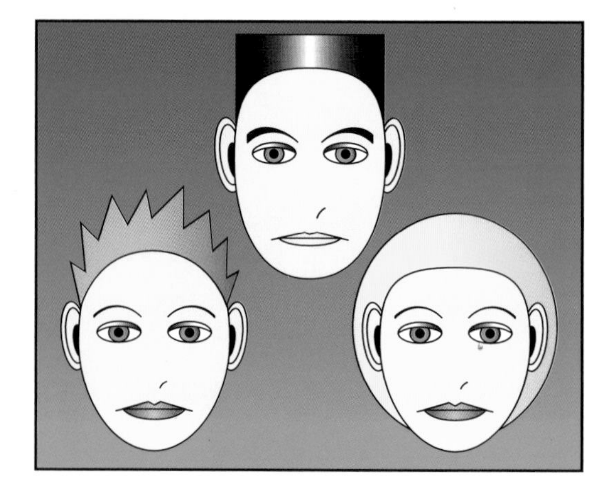

Three – a blond, a redhead and a brunette.

Locker Shocker

Rating 2 Points

How can Brad so easily recall this series of numbers, 21814, which he uses as a code for his locker?

Locker Shocker - Solution

A	B	C	D	E	F	G	H	I
1	**2**	3	**4**	5	6	7	8	9

J	K	L	M	N	O	P	Q	R
10	11	12	13	14	15	16	17	**18**

The letters BRAD are respectively the 2nd, 18th, 1st, and 4th, letters of the alphabet.

Colour Blind

Rating 1 Point

I have 25 ties equally divided into five different colours. If I were blindfolded, how many would I have to pick out to be sure of having one of each colour?

Colour Blind - Solution

21.

Duck Dilemma

Rating 1 Point

Two ducks in front of a duck, two ducks behind a duck and one duck in the middle. How many ducks?

Duck Dilemma - Solution

There are three ducks.

Crazy Counting

Rating 2 Points

I've got ten or more daughters.

I've got less than ten daughters.

I've got at least one daughter.

If only one of these statements is true, how many daughters have I got?

Crazy Counting - Solution

I've got ten or more daughters.

I've got less than ten daughters.

I've got at least one daughter.

If only one statement is true, there must be no daughters.

Loyalty Bonus

Rating 2 Points

Ken has had a very successful summer with his ice-cream stand on the sea front. He has a total of $200 bonus pay for his three employees. To his longest serving employee he wishes to give twice as much as to the second longest serving employee who in turn is to receive twice as much as the last employee. What are the nearest figures to the full dollar with which he can achieve this and how much will he have left from the $200?

Loyalty Bonus - Solution

$112, $56 and $28. He has $4 left.

First Move

Rating 2 Points

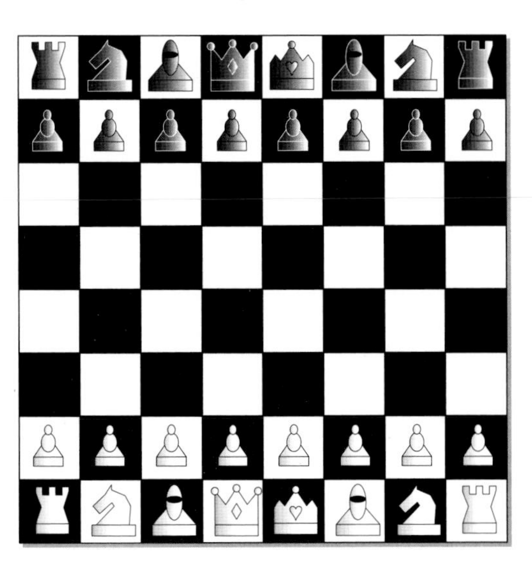

A chess board has been set up as shown with white moving up the board. Can we say if any moves have already been made?

First Move - Solution

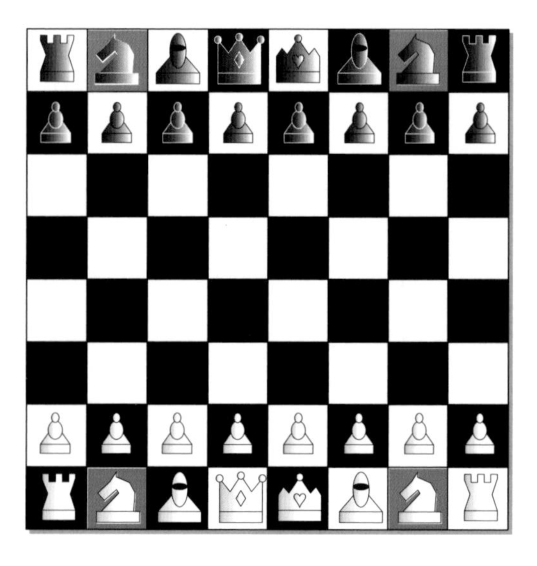

It is not possible to say if moves have occurred. Either the game has not started or both sides have moved a knight or knights, with all knights subsequently returning to their respective home ranks.

Sneaky Cipher

Rating 2 Points

RXRSDLZSHB

Most codes are quite systematic.
Can you work this one out?

Sneaky Cipher - Solution

SYSTEMATIC

"Systematic" - each letter is represented by the previous one in the alphabet.

Breaking Point

Rating 1 Point

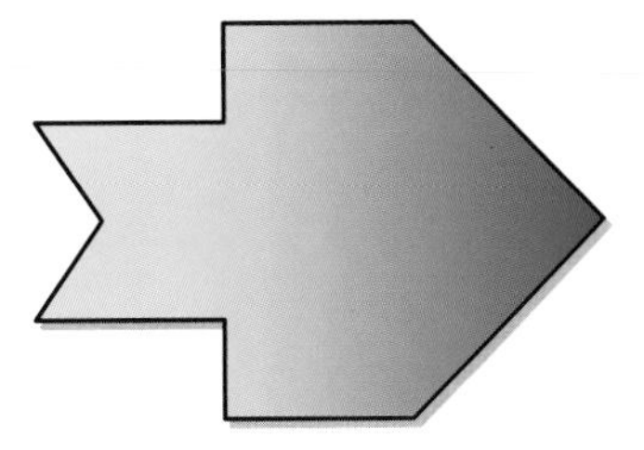

Cut this arrow into two pieces and, by moving only one piece, point the arrow in the opposite direction.

Breaking Point - Solution

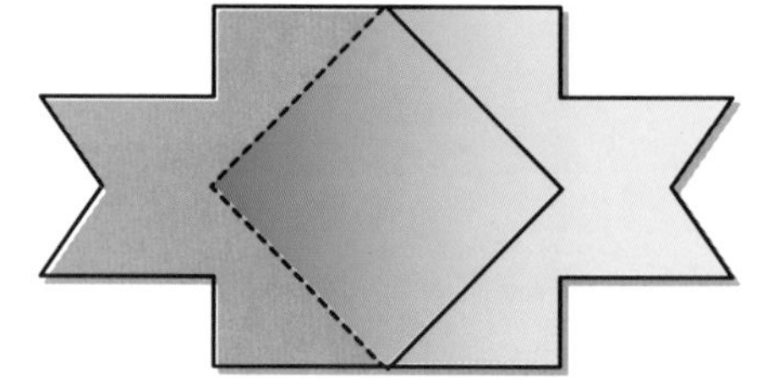

Cut the arrow along the dotted line then move the tail piece to the right-hand-side as shown.

Family Portrait

Rating 3 Points

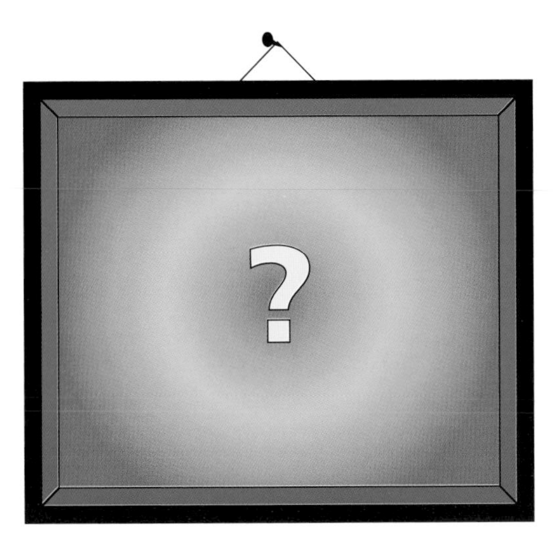

The mother, father, son, daughter, uncle, aunt, brother, sister, cousin, nephew, and niece of a family are all present at a family gathering. A photo is taken of them all. What is the least number of people in the photo?

Family Portrait - Solution

There are four people in the photo. A brother and a sister, the brother's son and the sister's daughter.

Odd One Out

Rating 1 Point

ABCDE
FGHIJK
MNOPQ
RSTUV
WXYZ

What seasonal message is this?

Odd One Out - Solution

Noel - There is no "L"!

Measuring Madness

Rating 2 Points

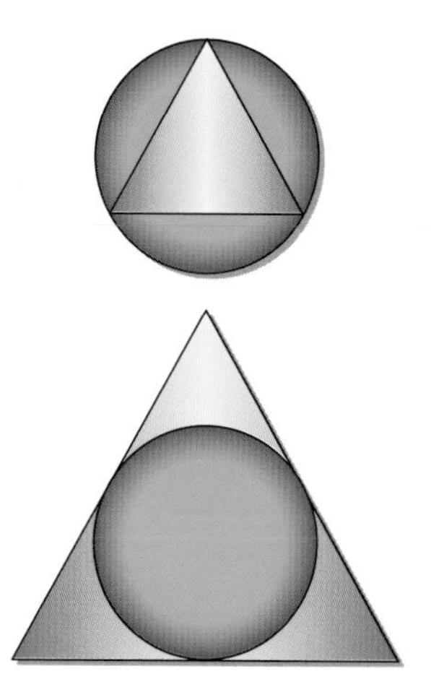

A set of kitchen containers, all 8in (203.2mm) high have very thin sides. The cross sections of the containers show two equilateral triangles that fit inside and outside the third circular container. If the smallest container holds exactly 1 pint (0.57litres) of milk, approximately how much does the largest container hold?

Measuring Madness - Solution

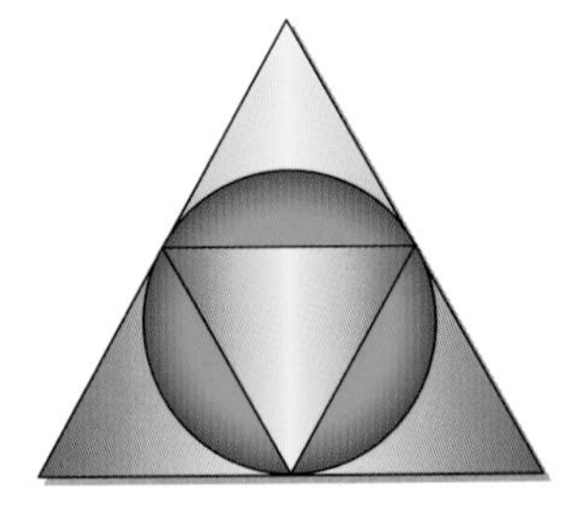

Four pints (2.27litres). This can be seen from the diagram, where four equal triangles make up the larger triangle.

To score any points in this chapter, you need to have provided the correct solution to each puzzle within three minutes of having read the question.

To see individual ratings for each puzzle – see under the title of each question. Once you have completed the chapter, turn to page 54, for help adding up your score.

Then turn to page 99 to start Chapter 3.

Chapter 2 - Scoring

Puzzle points for correct answer

Key Quandary	**2**	Horror Struck	**3**
Passing Trains	**1**	Mystery Theft	**2**
Latin Lesson	**2**	Cross Section	**1**
Mystery Shapes	**1**	Anniversary Anomaly	**2**
Chemical Crank	**1**	Match of Wits	**1**
Clean Cut	**1**	Marathon Run	**3**
Critical Choice	**3**	Face in the Crowd	**3**
Gridlock	**2**	Multiple Choice	**1**
Single Status	**3**	Rectangle Riot	**1**
Guinea Pig Poser	**1**	Bottom Dollar	**2**
Big Breakfast	**3**	Stake 100	**1**

YOUR TOTAL ___ / **40**

Key Quandry

Rating 2 Points

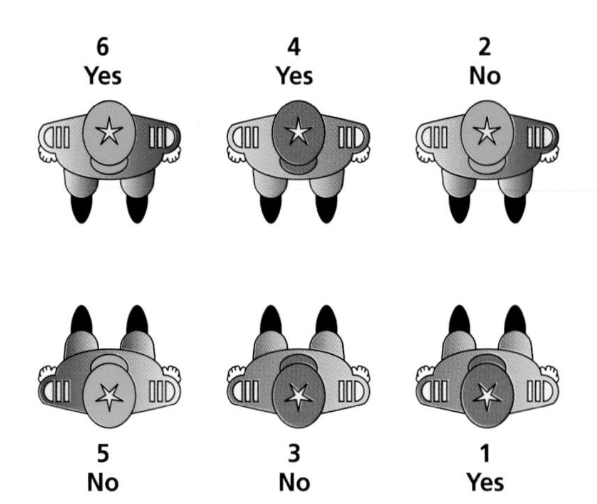

When on sentry duty the six guards of Leguna, three red and three blue, protect the castle gate as shown. One of the guards holds the key to the gate. Either all three red guards tell the truth and all three blue guards lie or vice versa. When asked the question, *"Is the key in the sentry box next to or opposite your own?".* the responses shown were given. Where is the key?

Key Quandry - Solution

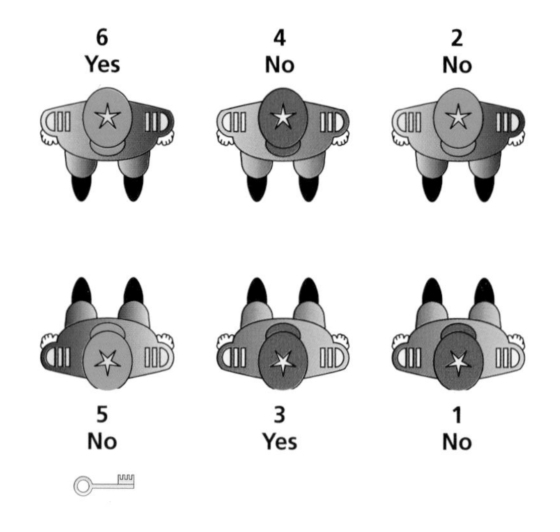

Guard number five holds the key and the red guards lied.

Passing Trains

Rating 1 Point

A London train bound for Manchester leaves London at 12 noon travelling at 80 miles an hour while a Manchester train bound for London leaves Manchester at 1pm travelling at 90 miles an hour. Which train is nearer to London when they meet?

Passing Trains - Solution

Neither. It doesn´t matter how fast the trains were travelling, they are both exactly the same distance from London when they meet.

Latin Lesson

Rating 2 Points

A class of students - Mary, Ian, Craig, Vernon, Derek, Belinda, and Laura - meets up for their first Latin lesson. After introducing each other, the teacher points out that Belinda is the odd one out. Why?

Latin Lesson - Solution

All the others have names that begin with a Roman Numeral.

Mystery Shapes

Rating 1 Point

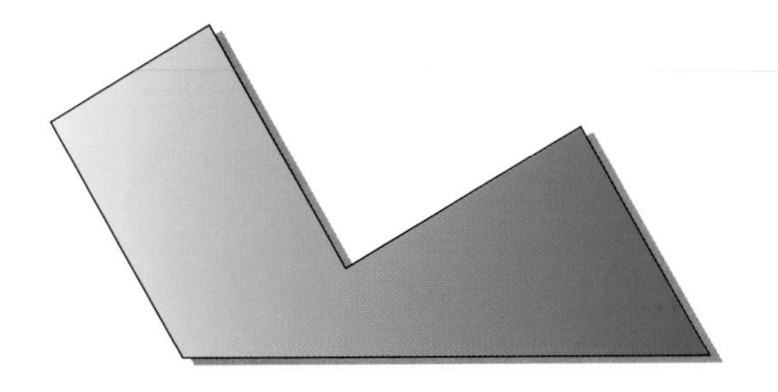

Fit four of these identical pieces together to make a hexagon.

Mystery Shapes - Solution

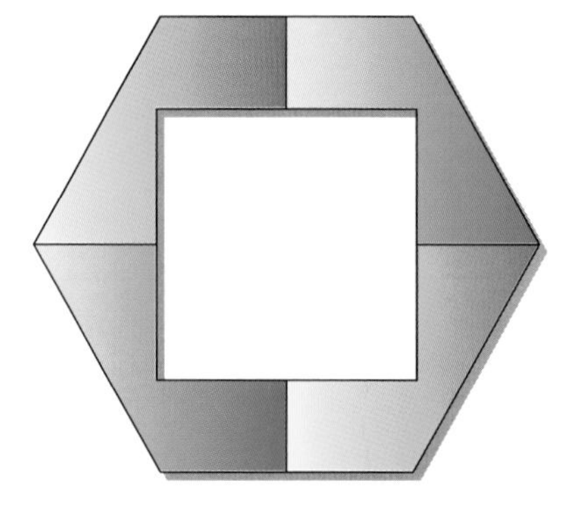

Two pieces are turned over and they fit together as shown.

Chemical Crank

Rating 1 Point

What liquid is this?

Chemical Crank - Solution

H^2O ie Water

Clean Cut

Rating 1 Point

What object can you cut clean through, and be left with one object with two ends?

Clean Cut - Solution

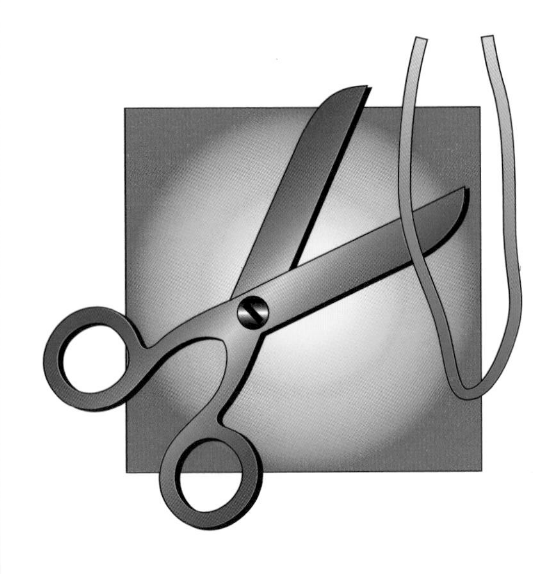

Any kind of loop.

Critical Choice

Rating 3 Points

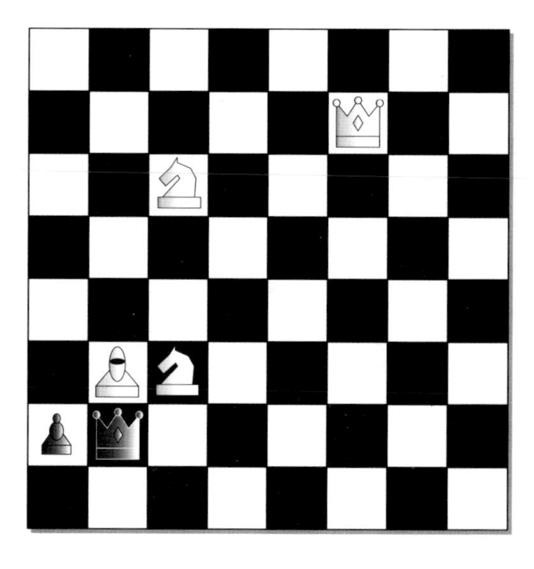

White is moving up the board. White is now going to take the black pawn, to prevent its queening, and then White wins. Does it matter whether he captures with the bishop or with the knight?

Critical Choice - Solution

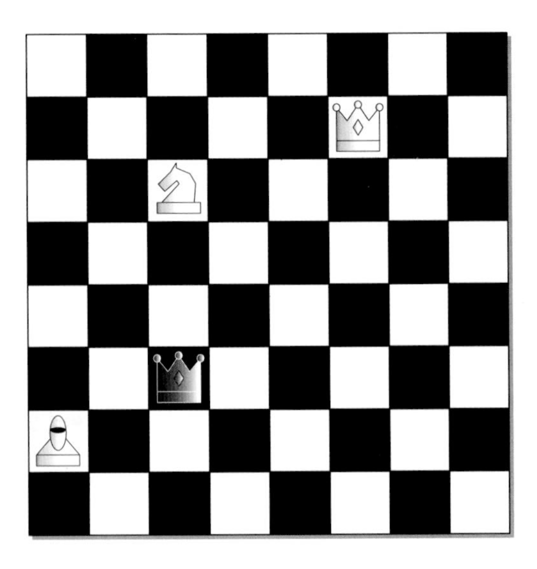

White must capture the pawn with the bishop (allowing the black king to take a knight). If White captured with the knight, Black would take the bishop with his king and the game would be drawn: a king, bishop and knight can together force the mate of a lone king, but a king and two knights cannot.

Gridlock

Rating 2 Points

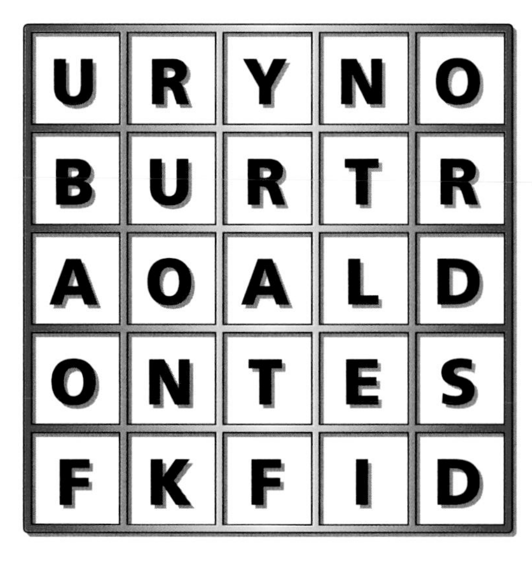

To read this secret message you must move from letter to letter like a knight in chess, visiting each letter only once. The message begins at the bottom left corner (F) of the grid. Thus the first move is either O or T. Continue in this way and spell out the hidden message.

Gridlock - Solution

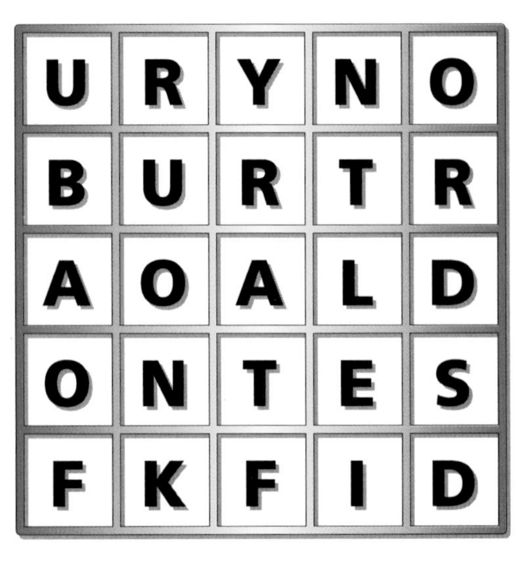

The message reads:
"Four old tarts found in bakery."

Single Status

Rating 3 Points

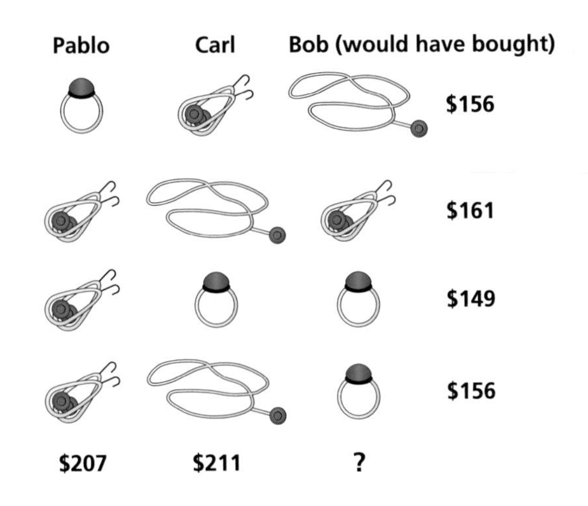

Fiona and Jayne took their boyfriends, Pablo and Carl, shopping. Pablo spent $207 on jewellery for Fiona, and Carl spent $211 on jewellery for Jayne. Their friend Bob, who is single, tagged along. If he had a girlfriend, he would have bought a necklace, earrings and two rings. How much has he saved by being young, free and single?

Single Status - Solution

Pablo	Carl	Bob (would have bought)	
			$156
			$161
			$149
			$156
$207	$211	**$204**	

Bob has saved $204.

Guinea Pig Poser

Rating 1 Point

Sally loves her guinea pigs. She has a number of them. They are either brown, black or white. Some are long-haired and some are short-haired. There are more brown than any other colour. She has an equal number of brown long-haired and brown short-haired guinea pigs. All but three are short-haired. There are twice as many brown long-haired as white long-haired guinea pigs. There are also three times as many black guinea pigs as white ones. How many guinea pigs does Sally have?

Guinea Pig Poser - Solution

Sally has eight guinea pigs.

Big Breakfast

Rating 3 Points

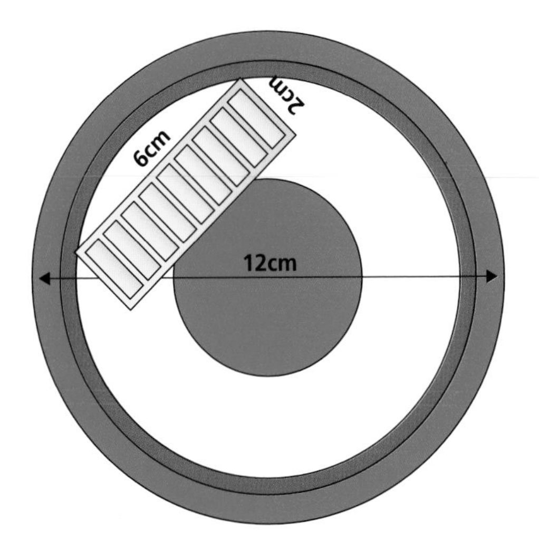

How many wheat bricks, 0.5cm (0.19in) thick, and measuring 2cm (0.78in) by 6cm (2.36in), will fit into a cereal bowl that is 12cm (4.72in) in diameter, laying flat, without one on top of another?

Big Breakfast - Solution

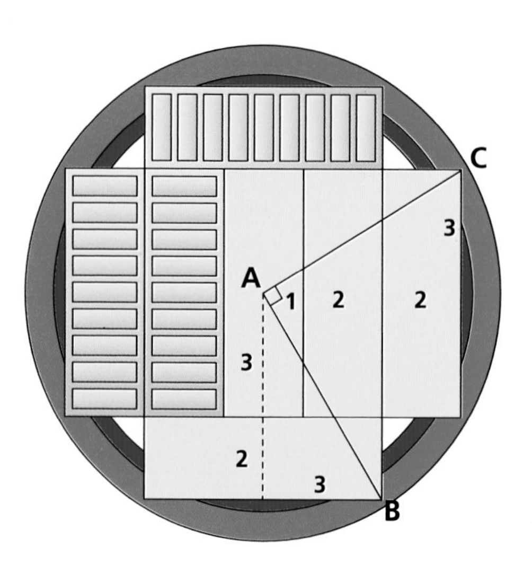

Seven - as shown.
Using pythagoras both A to B and
A to C equal $\sqrt{34}$ = 5.83cm (2.30in)

Horror Struck

Rating 3 Points

What is Shakespeare's Juliet saying, in the shock of realisation, in the coded message above?

Horror Struck - Solution

A	B	C	D	E	F	G	H	I	J	K	L	M
O	Q	S	U	W	Y	Z	X	V	T	R	P	N

The table above was used to encode Juliet's words. The second half of the alphabet was written underneath the first half of the alphabet starting with N on the left hand side, then O on the right, P on the right underneath L, Q underneath B on the left and so on.

Mystery Theft

Rating 2 Points

When the family jewels were stolen from inside a vat of vinegar and oil, my brother immediately suspected my sister's widow, but I knew this was wrong. How?

Mystery Theft - Solution

My sister cannot possibly have a widow.

Cross Section

Rating 1 Point

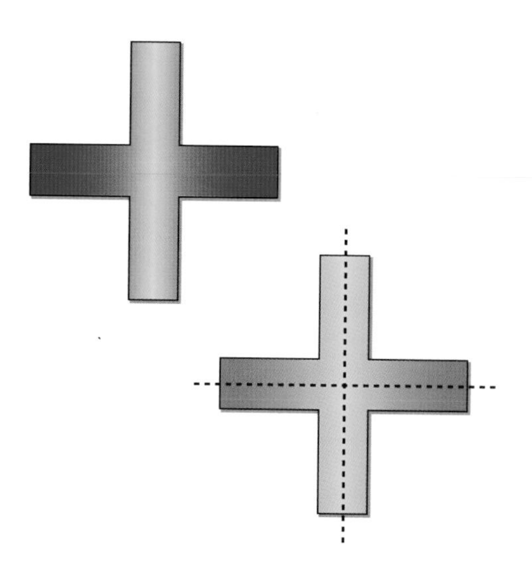

There are two ways to divide this shape into four equal parts with just two cuts. One way is shown, can you find the other?

Cross Section - Solution

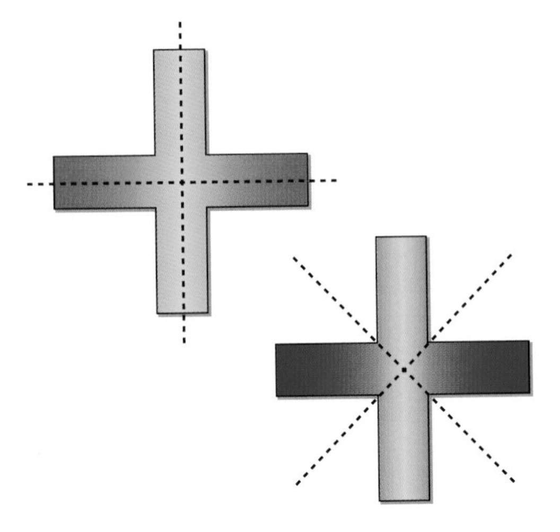

The two cuts are made as shown in the diagram.

Anniversary Anomaly

Rating 2 Points

Two days ago Bert was 20. Next year he will be 23. How can this be possible?

Anniversary Anomaly - Solution

Today is the first of January. Bert's birthday was on the 31st of December, yesterday, when he was 21. The day before yesterday he was 20, he will be 22 this year and 23 next year.

Match of Wits

Rating 1 Point

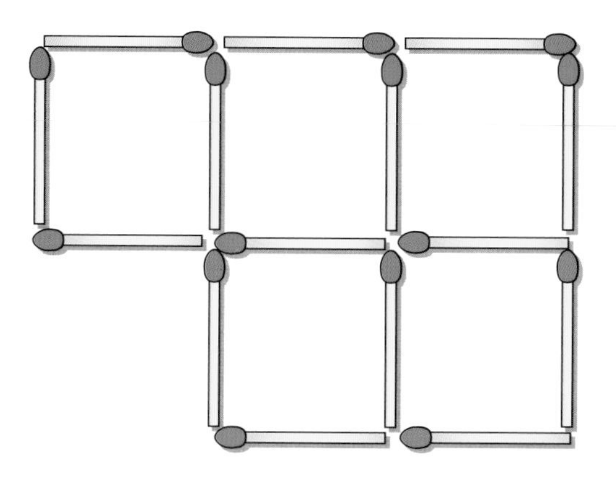

Fifteen matches have been laid out as shown, forming five equal squares. Remove three matches to leave only three squares.

Match of Wits - Solution

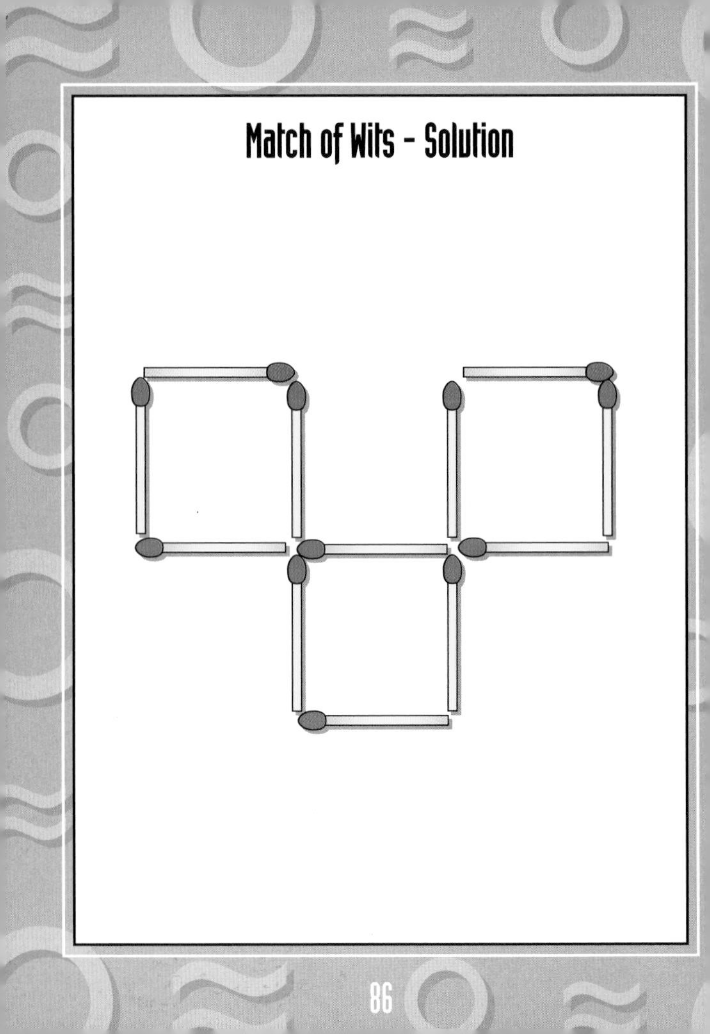

Marathon Run

Rating 3 Points

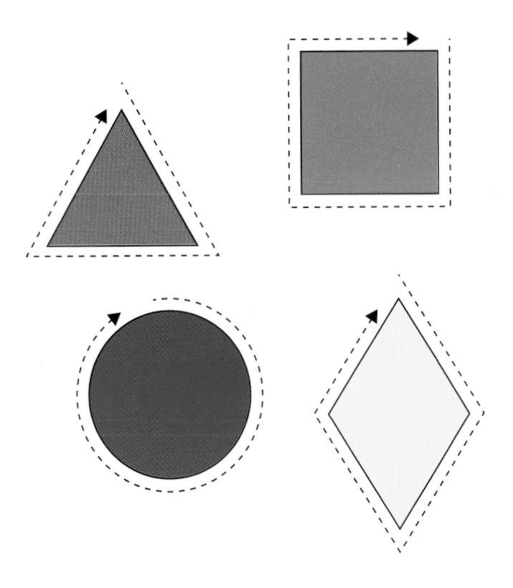

A runner training for a marathon likes to vary his daily run, but always runs the same distance of 16 miles. His routes, which form the perimeter of various mathematical shapes, are as shown. Which one enclosed the largest area?

Marathon Run - Solution

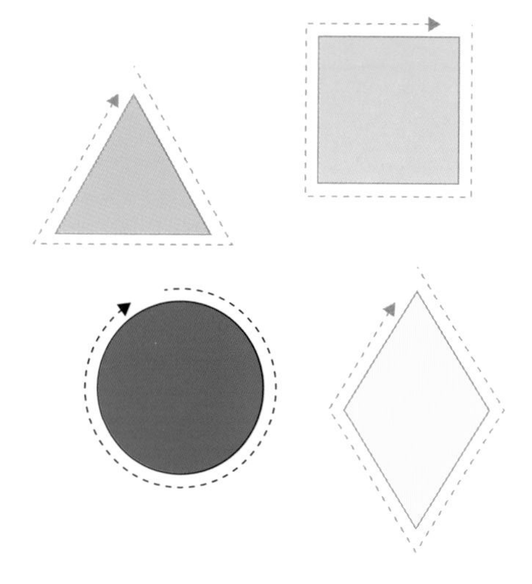

The circle with an area of approximately 20.4 ($\frac{64}{\Pi}$) square miles.

Face in the Crowd

Rating 3 Points

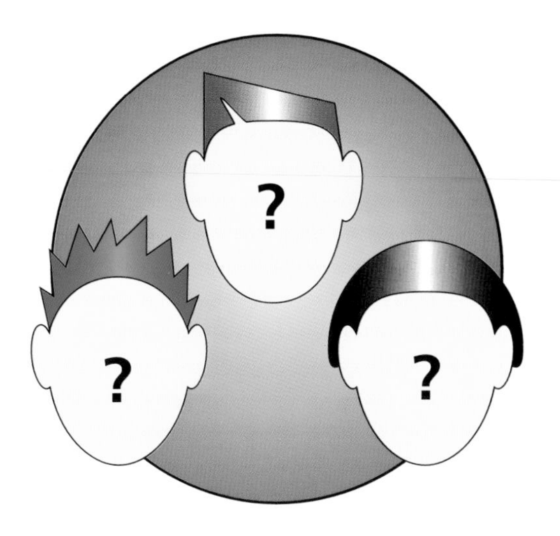

I had to meet an Australian, an American and a Canadian at the airport. One of them was called Hank, and as they approached I identified him immediately, despite never having met any of them before. How?

Face in the Crowd - Solution

The other two were women called Sandra and Emily.

Multiple Choice

Rating 1 Point

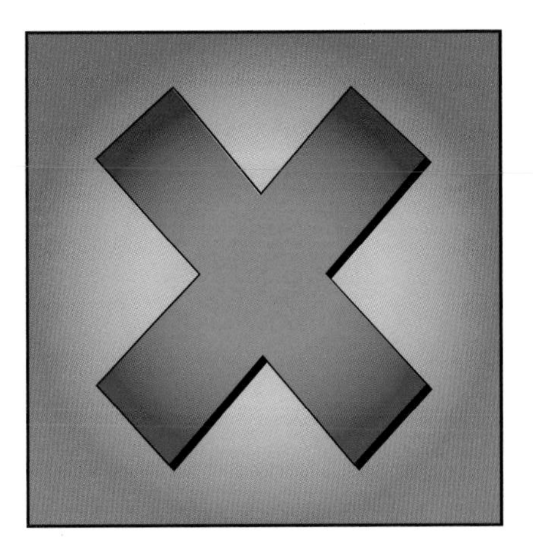

What do you get if you multiply all the non-negative integers less than 10 together?

Multiple Choice - Solution

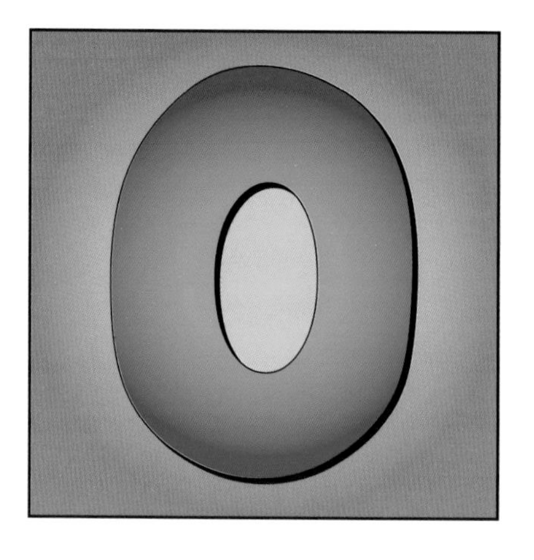

Zero.

Rectangle Riot

Rating 1 Point

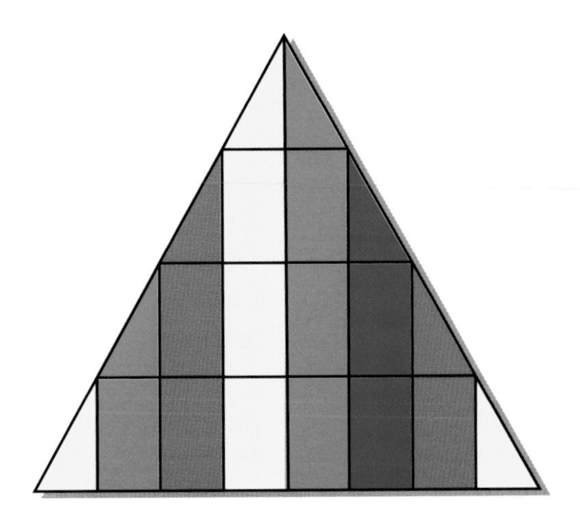

How many rectangles are there?

Rectangle Riot - Solution

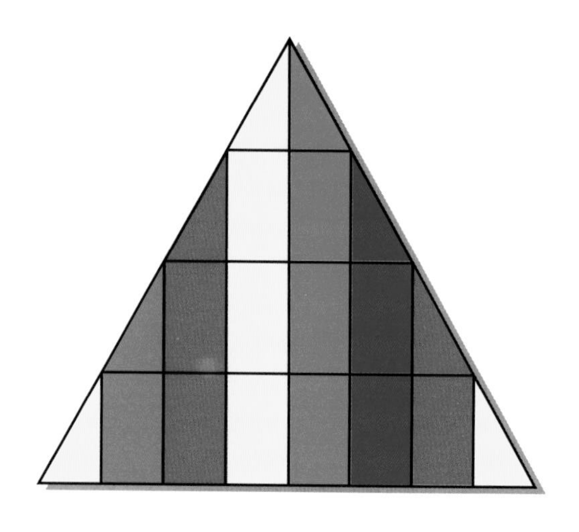

50.

Bottom Dollar

Rating 2 Points

If you have the same amount of money as your friend, how much should you give him so that he will have $10 more than you?

Bottom Dollar - Solution

$5.

Stake 100

Rating 1 Point

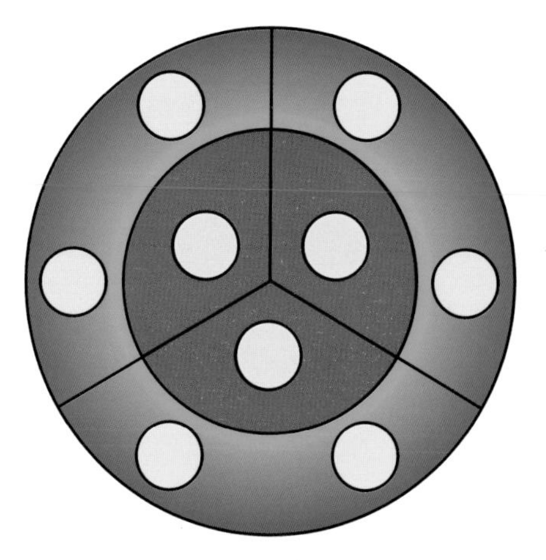

11, 12, 27, 28, 32, 40, 41, 49, 60.

Place the nine numbers above so that three in each third of the big circle add to 100. The three numbers in the inner circle must also add up to 100.

Stake 100 - Solution

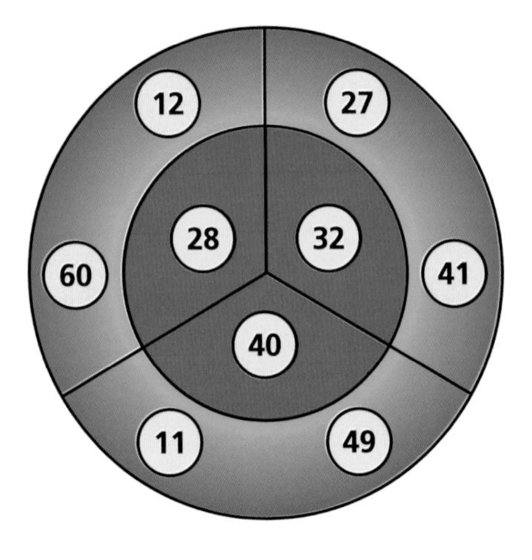

Chapter 3

To score any points in this chapter, you need to have provided the correct solution to each puzzle within five minutes of having read the question.

To see individual ratings for each puzzle – see under the title of each question. Once you have completed the chapter, turn to page 100, for help adding up your score.

Then turn to page 145 to start Chapter 4.

Chapter 3 - Scoring

Puzzle points for correct answer

Tricky Tuning	**3**	Hexagonal Hiatus	**2**
Thinking Backwards	**3**	Lager Lout	**1**
Pipe Connection	**3**	Sheep Fold	**2**
Foiled Escape	**2**	Chocolate Feast	**3**
Honeycomb Puzzle	**2**	Football Photo	**2**
Cryptic Calculation	**2**	Triangular Teaser	**2**
Bottle of Bordeaux	**1**	Time Difference	**3**
Overload	**1**	Pentagonal Problem	**1**
Quarter Quandary	**2**	Masterpiece Mystery	**3**
Shifting Shapes	**1**	Window Wizard	**3**
Rum Tumbler	**2**	Link Up	**1**

YOUR TOTAL

/ **45**

Rating 3 Points

3H WK2T2V 1QBWK3QJ
WK1W B45 Y1QW
3H WK2T2V 1QBWK3QJ 3
F1Q G4 L5VW F1NN 4Q P2
1QG 3NN V2QG 3W 1N4QJ
Y3WK N4X2 HT4P
P2 W4 B45

Can you decipher these famous song lyrics by John Lennon?

Tricky Tuning - Solution

A	B	C	D	E	F	G	H	I	J	K	L	M
1	D	F	G	2	H	J	K	3	L	M	N	P

N	O	P	Q	R	S	T	U	V	W	X	Y	Z
Q	4	R	S	T	V	W	5	X	Y	Z	B	C

The code table above was used to encode the song lyrics. First of all the vowels were numbered one to five, then each consonant was replaced by the next consonant but one in the alphabet.

Thinking Backwards

Rating 3 Points

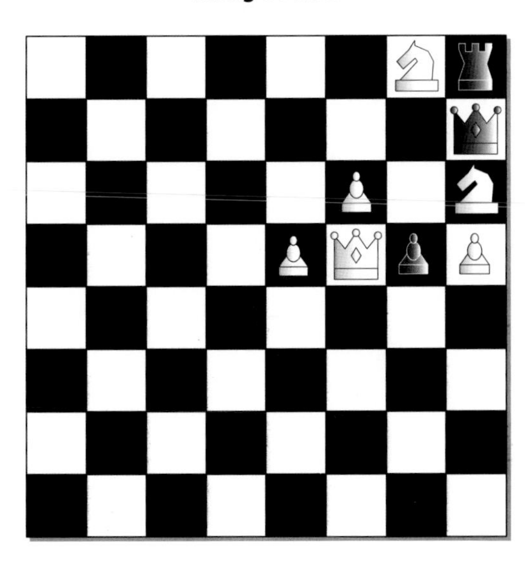

White is moving up the board. White can make a mating move at once. What is it?

Thinking Backwards - Solution

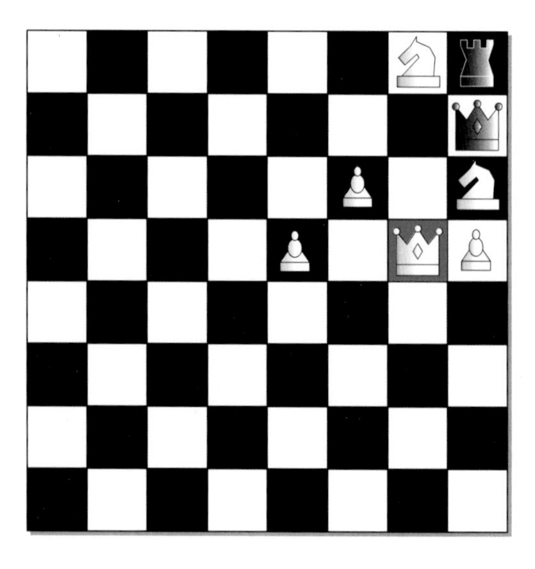

Black has just moved his pawn forward two squares – no other move was available to him. In particular, the pawn cannot have moved only one square, as it would have been checking the white king. So White can now take the pawn *en passant*, giving mate.

Pipe Connection

Rating 3 Points

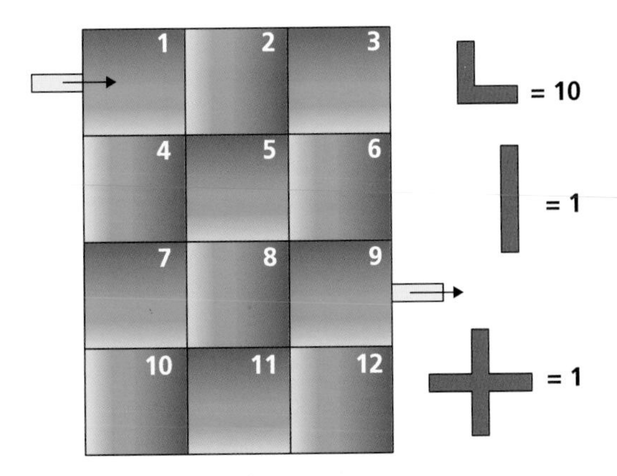

Twelve separate rooms in a block of flats are due to be served by under-floor heating, which will pass under all the rooms by means of connected pipes. The pipes are just long enough to run from the middle of one side of a room to the middle of another side. The engineer has at his disposal the pipe sections shown and the heat must enter and exit via the rooms indicated. Which room is most likely to be the warmest?

Pipe Connection - Solution

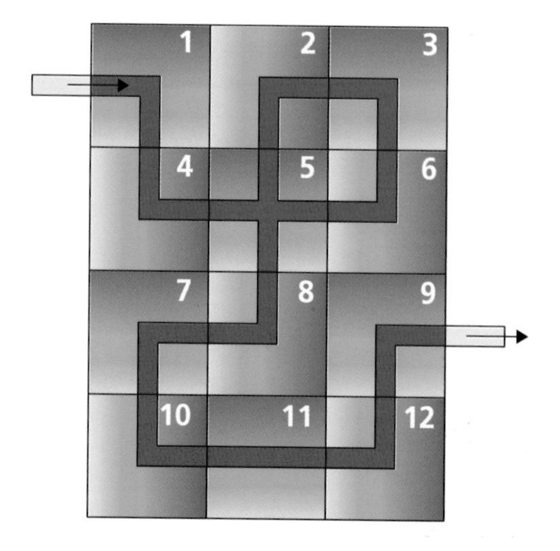

The only possible route is shown and Room 5 with a doubling of the pipes is most likely to be the warmest.

Foiled Escape

Rating 2 Points

Pete the prison guard, has discovered a coded message in the pillow of one of the prisoners. He is sure it concerns a possible escape plan and hopes to ascertain a meeting place. He knows Mike Green wrote the note, but can he crack the code?

Foiled Escape - Solution

A	B	C	D	E	F	G	H	I	J	K	L	M
★	Z	Y	X	◆	W	V	T	●	S	R	Q	P

N	O	P	Q	R	S	T	U	V	W	X	Y	Z
N	✪	M	L	K	J	H	▼	G	F	D	C	B

All consonants are interchanged with the letter immediately below or above it. The vowels are substituted according to the chart above.

Honeycomb Puzzle

Rating 2 Points

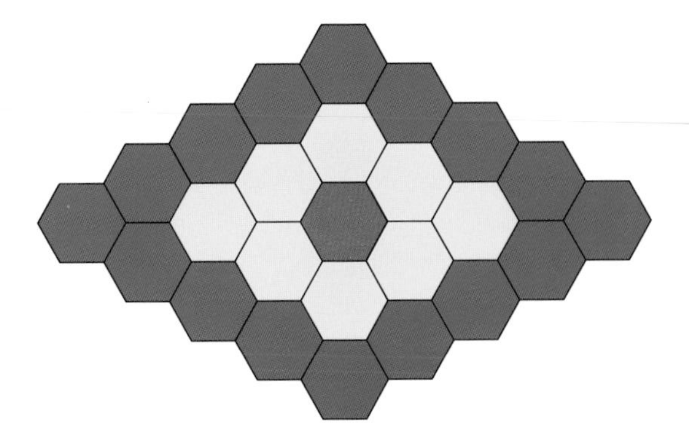

The diagram shows the inside of a bee hive, which constantly expands as the bees build more layers of hexagonal cells around each other. Can you determine the total number of cells after the next layer has been made, and guess what it might be after six layers have been added to the original cell?

Honeycomb Puzzle - Solution

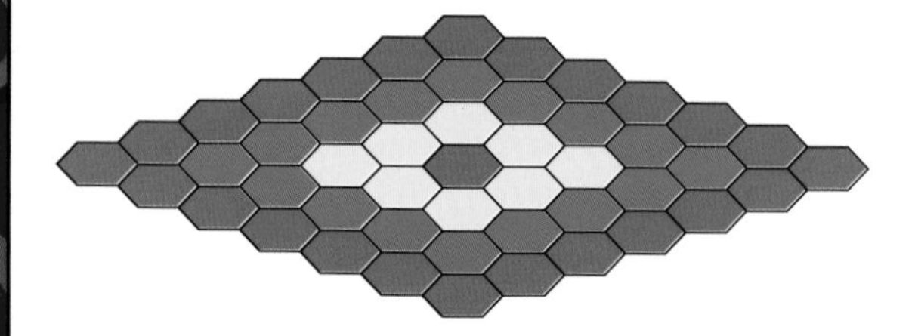

The total is 49 after a further 24 have been added. For n layers the total is $(2n+1)^2$ and therefore after 6 layers it is 169.

Cryptic Calculation

Rating 2 Points

Can you arrange the numbers 1 to 9 so that when they are added together they make the number 135?

Cryptic Calculation — Solution

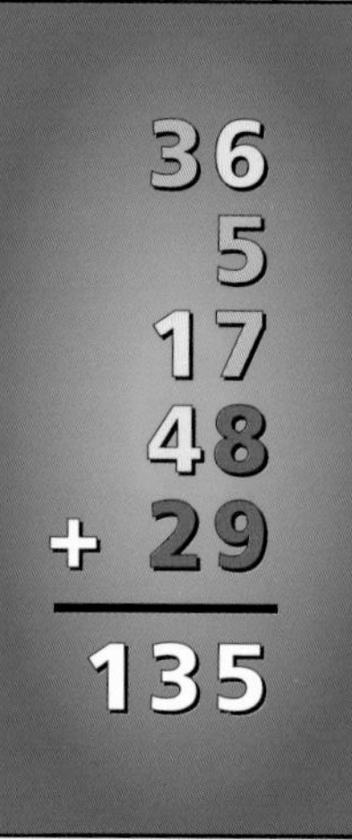

Bottle of Bordeaux

Rating 1 Point

Monsieur Giroud has a bottle of Bordeaux in his wine cellar that he has been saving for a suitable occasion. He decides to treat his family one Sunday and opens the bottle and shares it amongst his family to enjoy with their evening meal. Mr Giroud drinks one-third of his glass with his starter, then half of the remainder with his main course, then one quarter of what is left with his pudding. How much of the original glass does he have to savour with the cheese at the end of the meal?

Bottle of Bordeaux - Solution

He will have one quarter of his original glass left to savour with his cheese.

Overload

Rating 1 Point

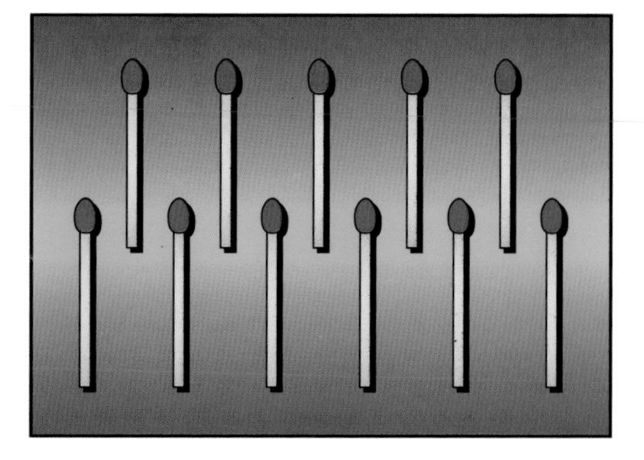

How can you add five matches to six matches and make nine?

Overload - Solution

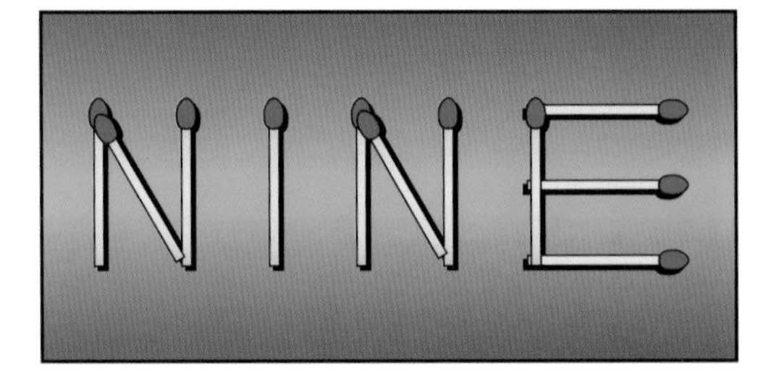

Place the six matches in a line then place the next five matches between these to make the word NINE.

Quarter Quandary

Rating 2 Points

Take the number 80 and divide it into four parts – four numbers which add up to 80 – so that:

If you add 3 to the first number
Subtract 3 from the second number
Multiply the third number by 3
And divide the fourth number by 3
You will be left with the same answer.

What are the original four numbers that make up eighty?

Quarter Quandary - Solution

12

18

5

45

The four numbers are 12, 18, 5, and 45.

Shifting Shapes

Rating 1 Point

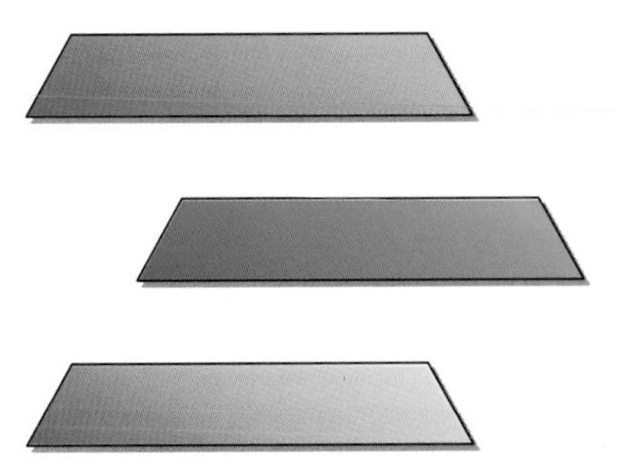

Using just the three identical shapes make two equilateral triangles.

Shifting Shapes - Solution

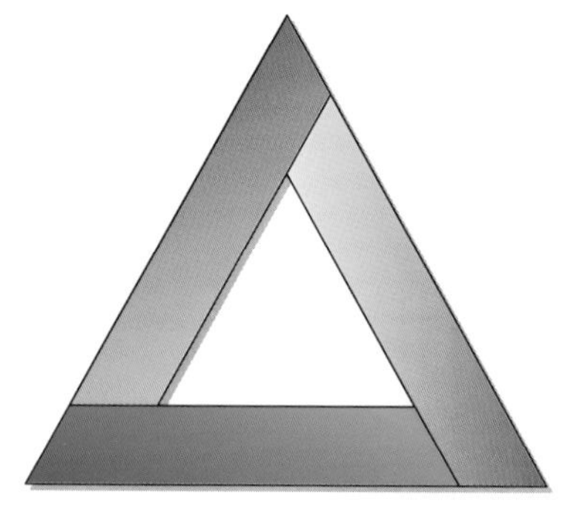

Rum Tumbler

Rating 2 Points

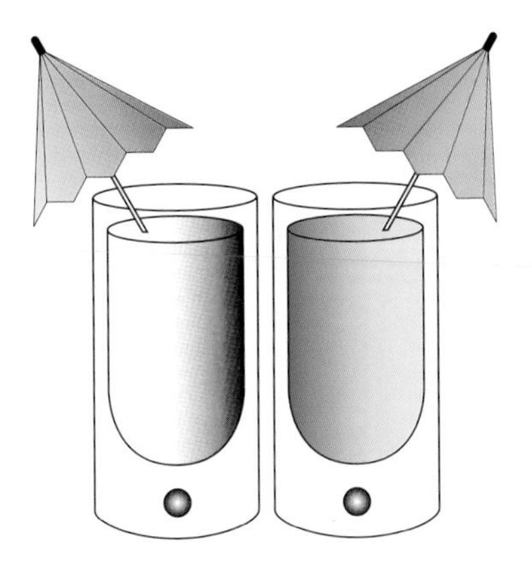

Two identical glasses of water have been placed on the table, one containing water and the other one rum. There is exactly the same volume of liquid in each glass. If you take a teaspoon of water and mix it into the rum and then take a teaspoonful from the glass of rum and mix it with the water, both glasses become adulterated. But which glass is more adulterated? Does the rum contain more water than the water or does the water contain more rum than the rum?

Rum Tumbler - Solution

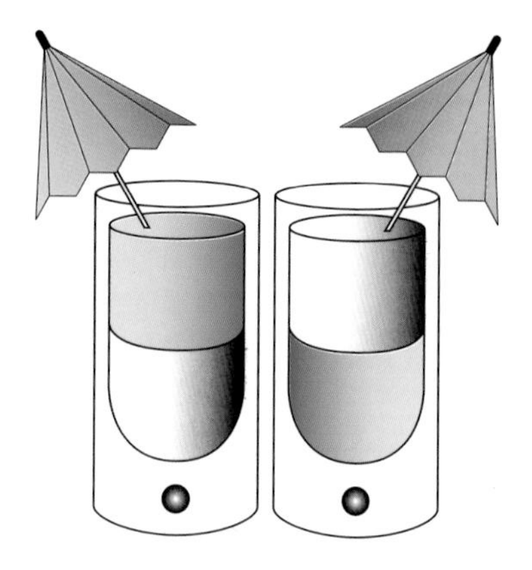

They are both equally polluted. The water contains exactly as much rum as the rum contains water. It does not make any difference how many exchanges are made or whether or not the liquids are stirred. As long as the volumes in the two glasses are the same, then any water not in the water glass must be in the rum and vice versa. The rum that it has replaced must be in the water glass. Therefore the water glass contains as much rum as the rum contains water.

Hexagonal Hiatus

Rating 2 Points

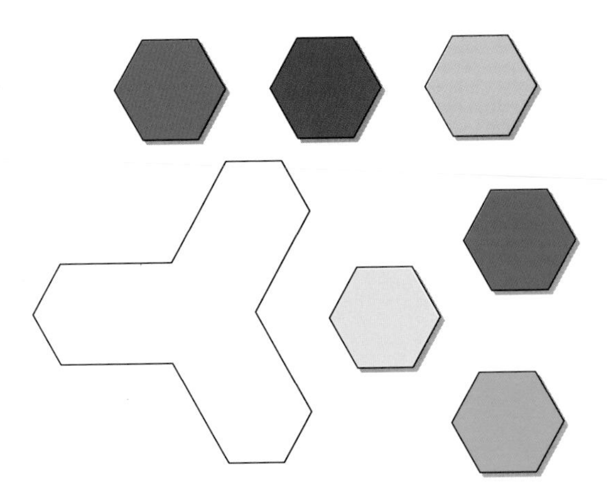

With the six identical hexagons how can I make the shape shown and still have one hexagon left over?

Hexagonal Hiatus - Solution

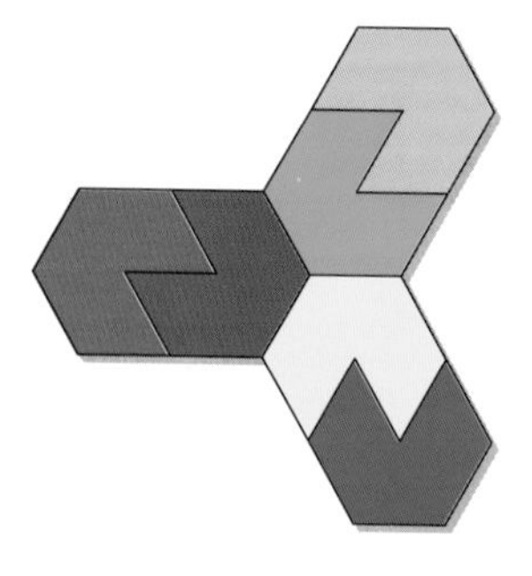

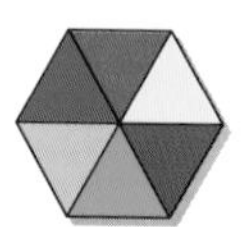

Cut the same shaped equilateral triangle from each and put together as shown.

Lager Lout

Rating 1 Point

A man spends $21 in a liquor store. The whisky cost twice as much as the beer, which cost twice as much as the soda water. How much was the beer?

Lager Lout - Solution

\$6. If the soda is X, the beer is $2X$ and the whisky is $4X$. If $7X = \$21$, $X = \$3$.

Sheep Fold

Rating 2 Points

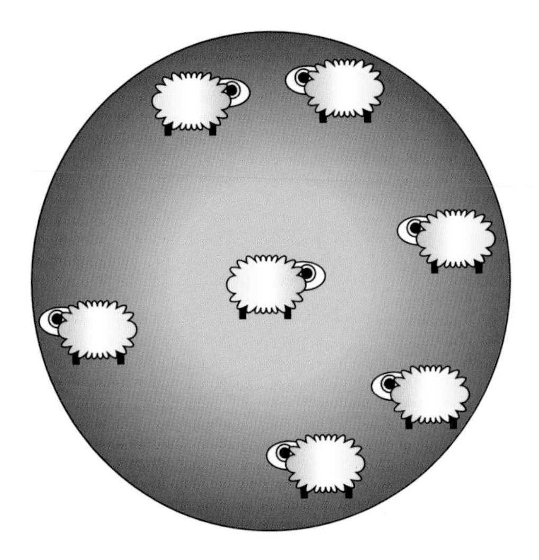

Farmer Giles's seven sheep are territorially minded. How should the farmer place three straight fences across the circular field so that each sheep is individually segregated?

Sheep Fold - Solution

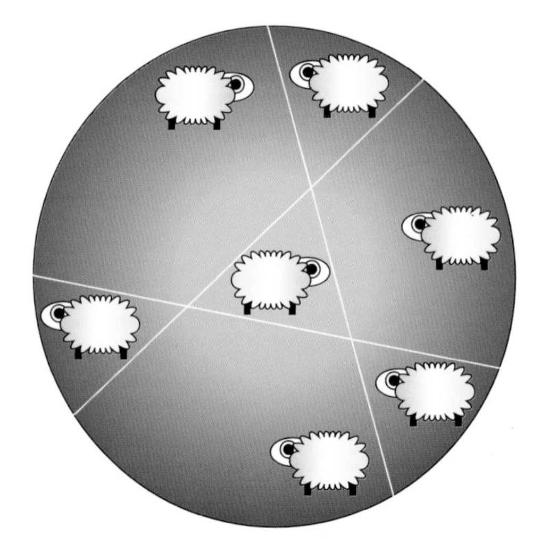

Chocolate Feast

Rating 3 Points

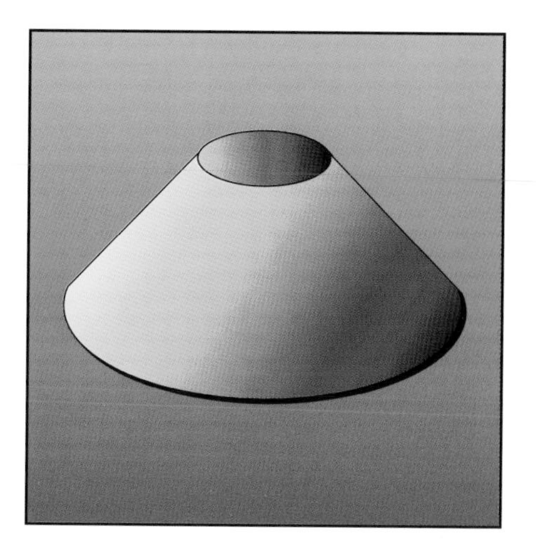

A chocolate sweet, shown, is 1cm (0.39in) high and measures 3cm (1.18in) in diameter at the base, and 1cm (0.39in) in diameter at the top. How many of these can you get into a box 1cm (0.39in) high that measures 20cm (7.87in) by 9cm (3.54in) and close the lid?

Chocolate Feast - Solution

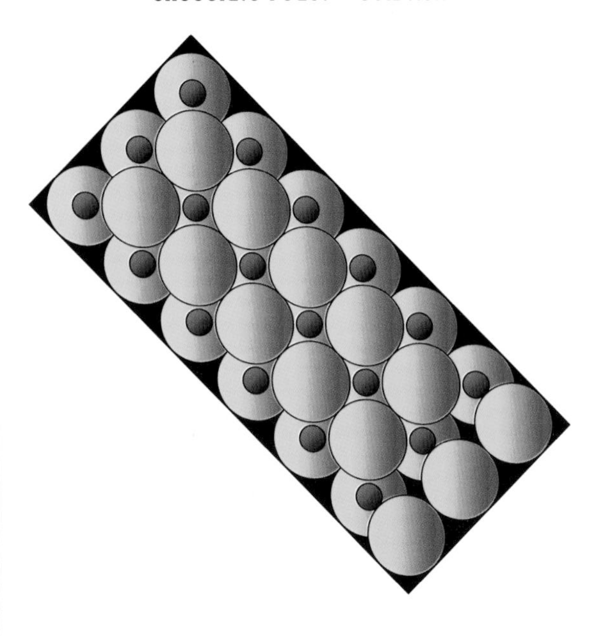

31. 18 with the larger side at the bottom and 13 upside down as shown.

Football Photo

Rating 2 Points

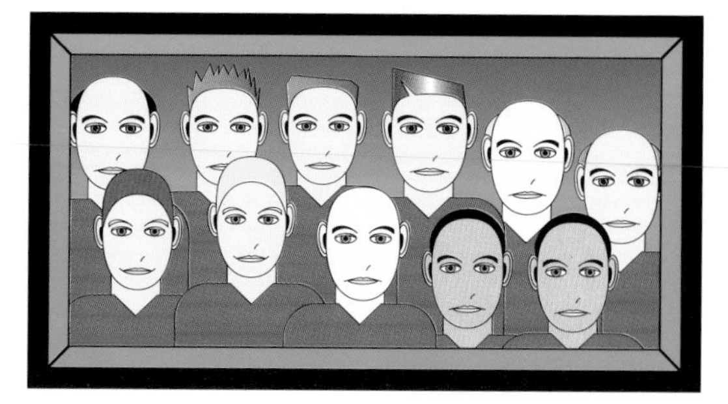

This picture shows the 11 members of the Flipside Whippets football team who won the local Worker's Cup. Five of this team are members of the Carlson family, but none of them is next to each other. They include Dominic, Eric, Ben, Thomas and Brian. Dominic, the captain, is in the centre of the photo. Eric stands closely behind his son Ben, and Thomas, who has no relatives immediately in front of him, is on his father Brian's left-hand-side. The Arnold twins who stand next to each other are not directly behind either of the Smart brothers who are good friends of Ben. Where was Brian?

Football Photo - Solution

Arnold
Eric **Twins** **Brian** **Thomas**

Ben **Dominic** **Smart**
Brothers

Brian stood where shown.

Triangular Teaser

Rating 2 Points

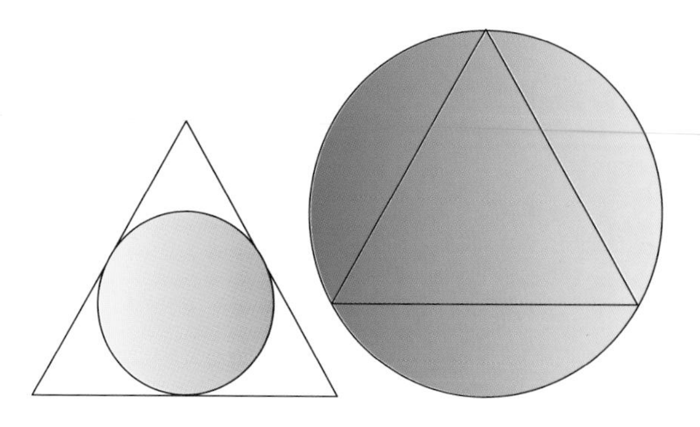

A set of containers, all 8in (20.32cm) high have very thin sides. The cross sections of the containers show two circles that fit inside and outside the third container, which is an equilateral triangle. If the smallest container holds exactly 2 pints (1.12litres) of milk, approximately how much does the largest container hold?

Triangular Teaser - Solution

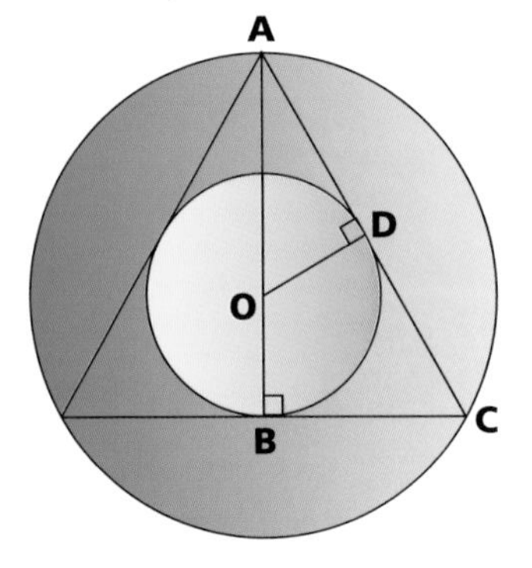

8 pints (4.48litres). From the diagram it can be seen that the two triangles ADO and ABC are exactly the same shape. The side AC is twice the length of the side BC, therefore the side OA is twice the length of the side OD. These are the radii of the circles. Hence the area ($\prod r^2$) of the larger circle is 4 times the area of the smaller circle.

Time Difference

Rating 3 Points

A standard Laguna clock is shown with the time just past midnight. Laguna clocks run on a different time scale to our own, with four complete revolutions during a day (24 hours = 12 Howers in Laguna) known as am, bm, pm and qm respectively (3.00qm being midnight). It is 9.15am GMT, what is the time in Laguna?

Time Difference - Solution

The time as shown on the clock is 1.10pm.

Pentagonal Problem

Rating 1 Point

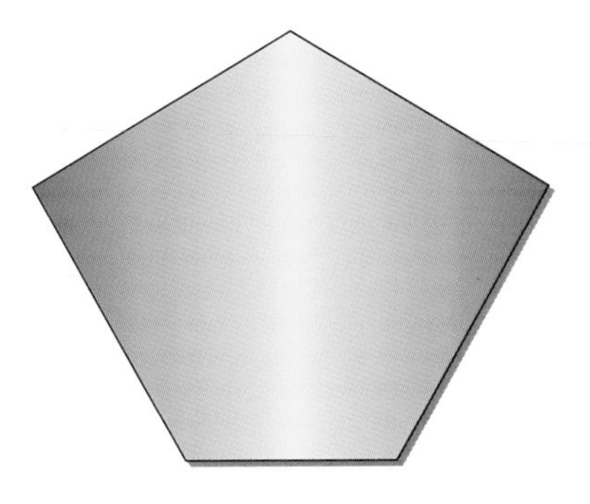

Make a regular hexagon with six of these symmetrical pentagons.

Pentagonal Problem - Solution

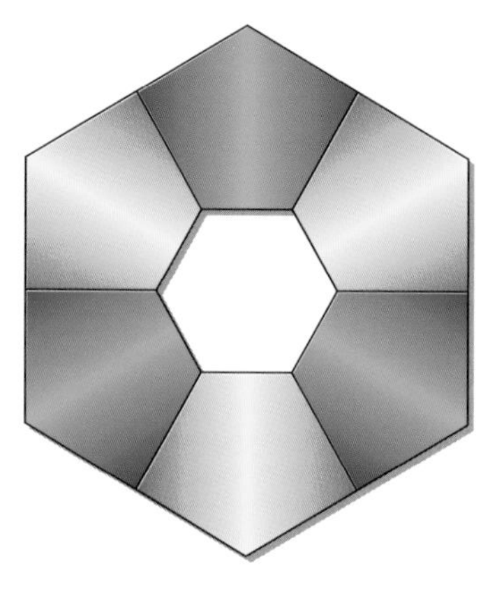

Two regular hexagons can be made as shown.

Masterpiece Mystery

Rating 3 Points

An artist is painting on a canvas measuring 2m (6.56ft) by 2m (6.56ft). He would like to cover half the canvas in a sky blue paint, but he also wants to leave a square section blank, which is still 2m (6.56ft) high and 2m (6.56ft) wide. Is it possible for him to do both?

Masterpiece Mystery - Solution

Yes, he can paint the canvas as shown.

Window Wizard

Rating 3 Points

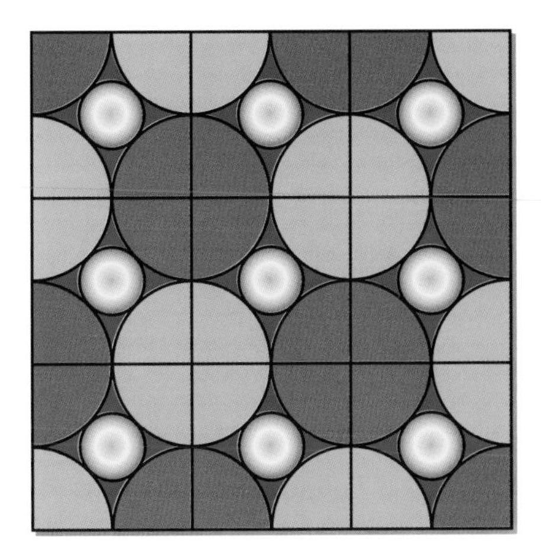

A stained glass window just over 12in (304.8mm) square has 9 symmetrical panes that are 4in (101.6mm) wide. If the lead boundary strip retaining the separate pieces of glass is an eighth of an inch (3.17mm) thick what area of glass is needed for the small orange circles? Assume that ∏ is 3.14.

Window Wizard - Solution

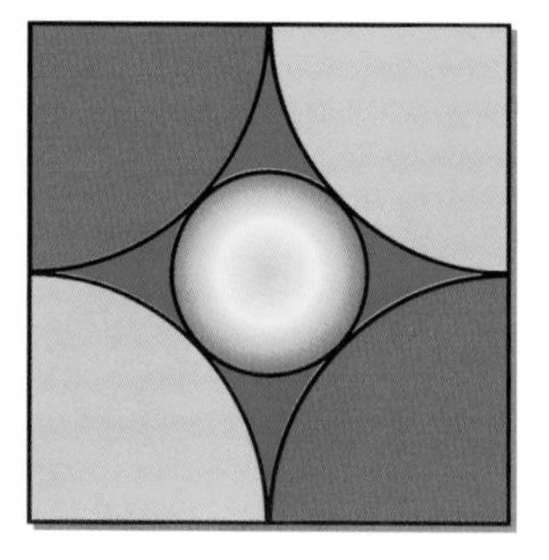

13.99 sq. in (355.35 square mm).
The diameter of each circle is $(4\sqrt{2} - 4) - 0.25$in,
giving a total area of 9 times Π times $(0.703)^2$ sq. in.

Link Up

Rating 1 Point

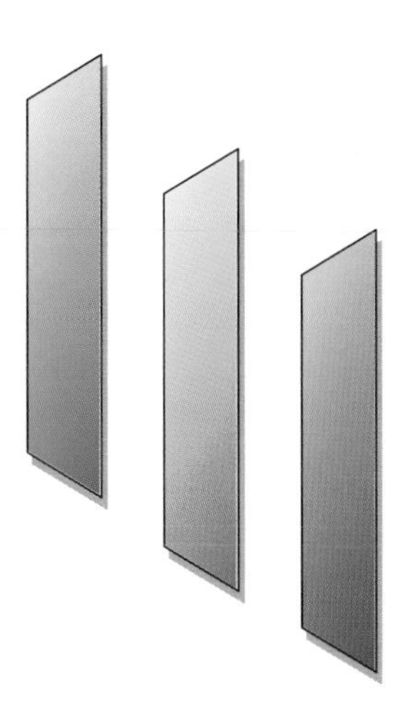

Using just the three identical shapes make a regular hexagon and an equilateral triangle.

Link Up - Solution

Chapter 4

To score any points in this chapter, you need to have provided the correct solution to each puzzle within ten minutes of having read the question.

To see individual ratings for each puzzle – see under the title of each question. Once you have completed the chapter, turn to page 146, for help adding up your score.

Then turn to page 191 to see your Overall Score.

Chapter 4 - Scoring

Puzzle points for correct answer

Puzzle	Points	Puzzle	Points
Lottery Triangle	**3**	Codenames	**3**
Art Movement	**2**	Frame Up	**2**
Lucky Letters	**2**	Champagne Surprise	**1**
Picnic in the Park	**1**	Double Dealing	**2**
Flying Colours	**2**	False Front	**3**
Ant Antics	**2**	F1 Quandary	**2**
Animal Mobile	**2**	Hoopla	**3**
Way-Out Wall	**2**	Close Call	**1**
Camouflage Caper	**1**	Winning Numbers	**2**
Pablo's Problem	**3**	Duke's Delight	**3**
Equal Terms	**2**	Cover Up	**1**

YOUR TOTAL

____ / **45**

Lottery Triangle

Rating 3 Points

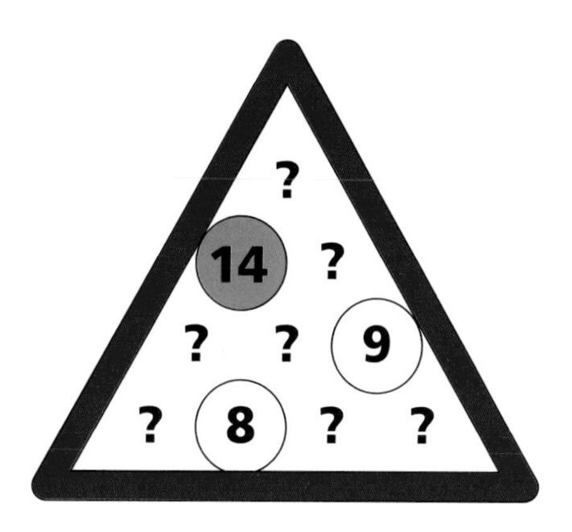

Lottery balls are numbered 1 - 9 white, 10 - 19 blue, 20 - 29 red, 30 - 39 green, and 40 - 49 yellow. Two balls of each colour are placed in a triangular rack as shown. The total of the numbers on the balls for the rows of 3 balls and rows of 4 balls is the same at 96. Fill in the missing balls.

Lottery Triangle - Solution

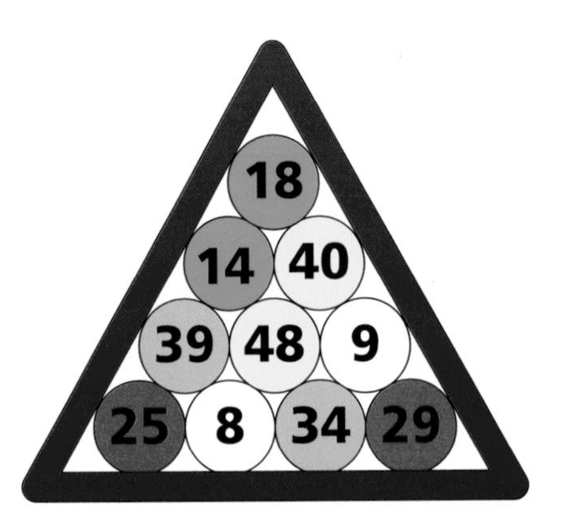

It can be seen that by deducting 8 and 9 from 96 the central ball could only be in the 40s. If it is 47 or below there will be two other yellow balls. Therefore it is 48. This determines the 34, 39 and 40 balls by subtraction. The values of the 3 remaining balls can be determined by letting one take the value of *x* and working round the outside.

Art Movement

Rating 2 Points

if 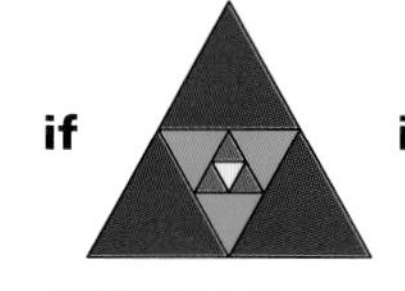 is to: 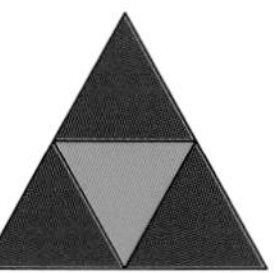

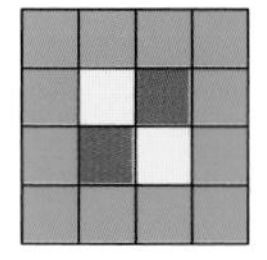 is to **?**

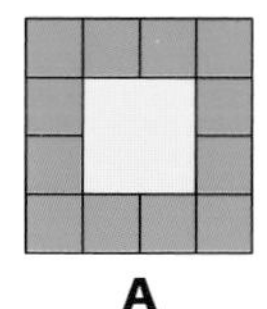

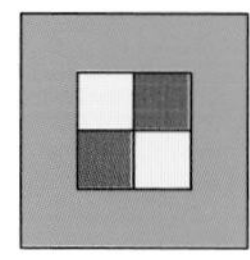

A **B** **C** **D**

Minimalist artist Pierre Maindrain thinks a triangular picture he has just painted is too complicated. He changes it as shown above. He likes the effect so much that he tries it on some other paintings. What happens when he does the same to this square painting?

Art Movement - Solution

if **is to:** 

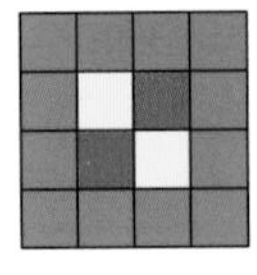 **is to ...**

C. He is left with nothing. The rule he has followed is to remove all the smallest versions of the outer shape from the painting.

Lucky Letters

Rating 2 Points

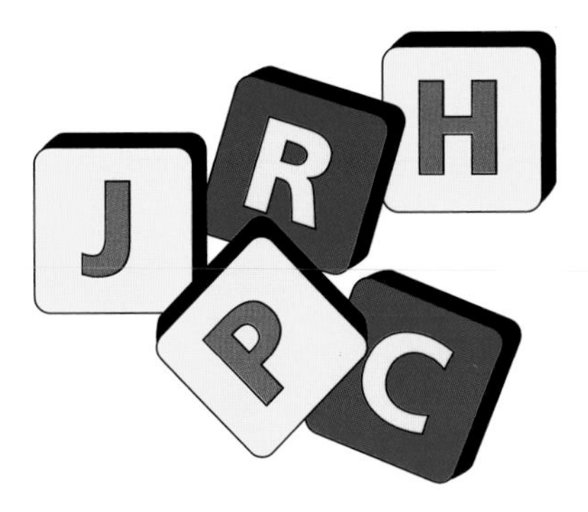

Six friends are playing a word game. To see who will start, they each draw a letter tile from a bag containing all the letters of the alphabet.

Anna pulls out a J
Simon pulls out an R
Lauren pulls out an H
Joe pulls out a P
Marie-Claire pulls out a C

Jaqueline's letter completes the sequence perfectly. What is it?

Lucky Letters - Solution

E. Starting from the middle of the alphabet, the boys go forwards the number of letters in their name. The girls go backwards the number of letters in their name.

Picnic in the Park

Rating 1 Point

Some of the residents of Spiral Street decide to go to a park to have a picnic. They travel there in two cars. Despite their different combinations of passengers, both carloads weigh exactly 445kg (981.04lb).

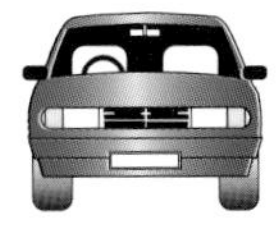

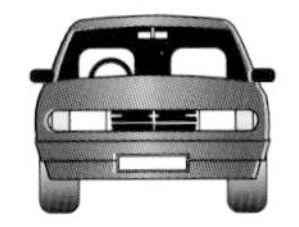

1	2
1 adult	3 adults
4 teenagers	2 teenagers
2 babies	5 babies
4 dogs	2 dogs

If an adult is three times heavier than a dog, and six babies weigh the same as one teenager, how heavy is an adult?

Picnic in the Park - Solution

One adult weighs 75kg (165.34lb).

Flying Colours

Rating 2 Points

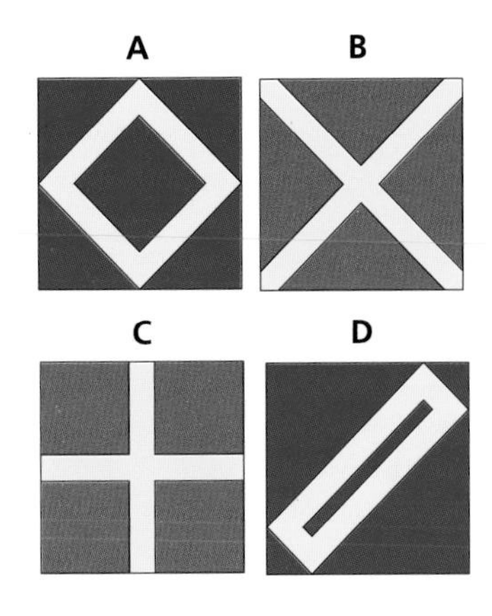

In the land of Laguna companies are allowed to have their own flags flying above their buildings, providing that they are 8 ft (2.44m) by 8 ft, have a red or blue background and a yellow stripe or connected band that is 1 ft wide (305mm). The law also requires that the area of the yellow band must not be more than 30% of the whole area of the flag. Which one of the flags shown infringes this last requirement?

Flying Colours - Solution

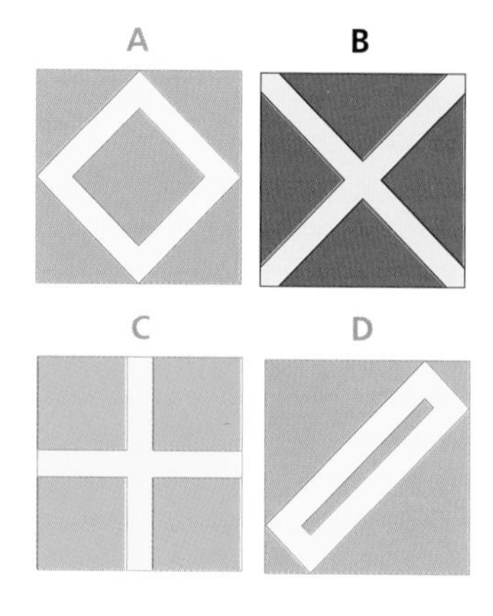

Flag (b), where the proportion is 32.2%.
For flags (a) and (d) it is 29.1% and for (c) it is 23.4%.

Ant Antics

Rating 2 Points

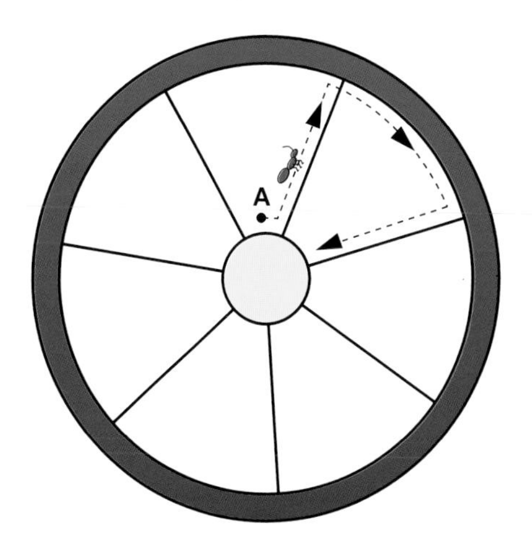

An ant stationed on the hub of a wheel (A) starts to walk in a clockwise direction, as shown, continuing up the spoke, along the inside of the rim, down the next spoke and so on. Midway along a spoke the ant traverses to its opposite side. If the radius of the hub is 2in (50.8mm) and the length of each spoke is 26in (660.4mm), approximately how far has the ant travelled when it first returns to its starting position? Assume that Π is 3.14.

Ant Antics - Solution

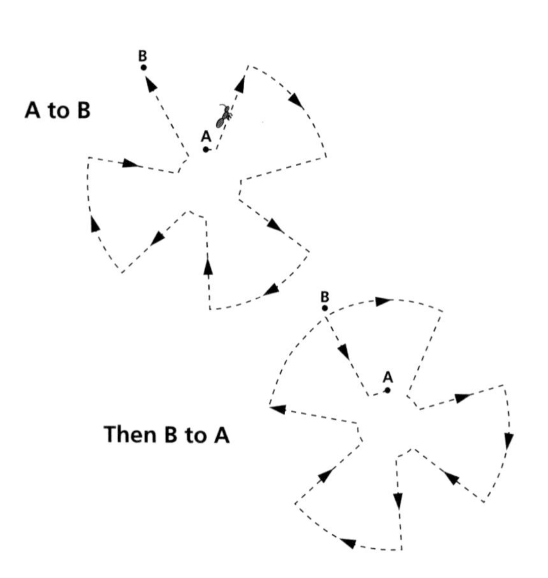

370.4in (9.4m). The ant travels the circumference of the hub and the inner rim once and twice the length of each spoke as shown.

Animal Mobile

Rating 2 Points

When constructing a children's mobile with 8 animals – a Zebra, a Camel, a Python, a Tiger, a Lemur, a Lion, a Hippo and a Panda – it was decided that animals with any of the same letters in their name should not be immediately above or below one another. If the Lemur is more than one place above the Python what animal is fifth from the top?

Animal Mobile - Solution

The Camel.
The only possible arrangement is as shown.

Way-Out Wall

Rating 2 Points

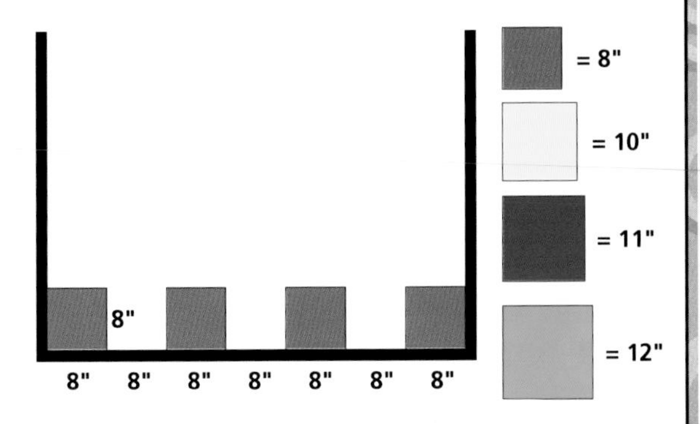

Jack has a large supply of different-sized cubic bricks available to make a wall between two posts and he wishes to use as few of these as possible. He starts the wall at one post using 8in (203.2mm) bricks and 8in gaps as shown. For strength each layer of bricks must overlap the layer below by at least one-quarter of the size of the brick below. At the 4th layer what is the minimum possible distance between the first brick and the post?

Way-Out Wall - Solution

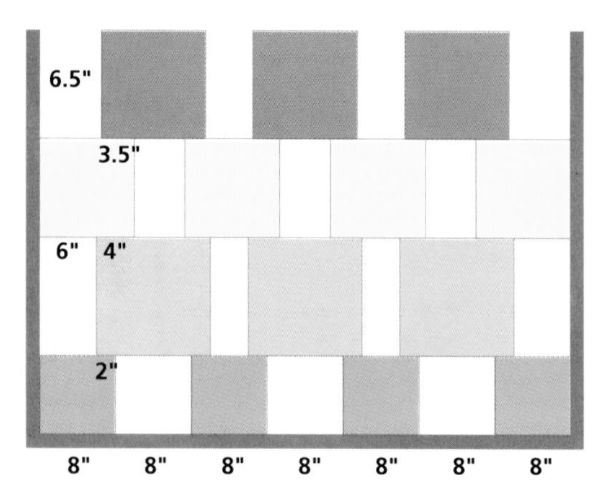

6.5in (165.1mm) as shown.

Camouflage Caper

Rating 1 Point

Papillo Spotticus, the spotted butterfly, comes in different sizes and various shades of orange and yellow. All varieties have exactly the same number of spots in the same places. Seven of these butterflies are shown partially hidden by leaves and undergrowth. How many spots does Papillio Spotticus have?

Camouflage Caper - Solution

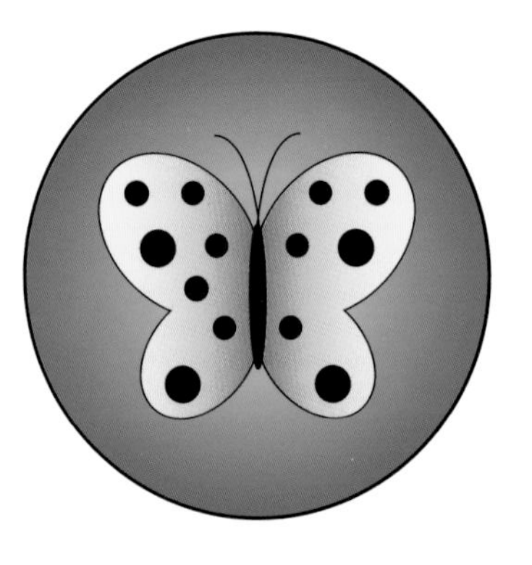

13 as shown.

Pablo's Problem

Rating 3 Points

Sitting on the school bus are seven boys and seven girls, with three vacant seats as shown. Another boy, Pablo, gets on the bus and sits in the first vacant seat, next to the window. He notices that there are the same number of girls in front of and behind him. If Pablo had sat in the next vacant seat he would have had the same number of boys in front of him, behind him and to his left, but more on his right-hand-side. What was the distribution of children before he got on?

Pablo's Problem - Solution

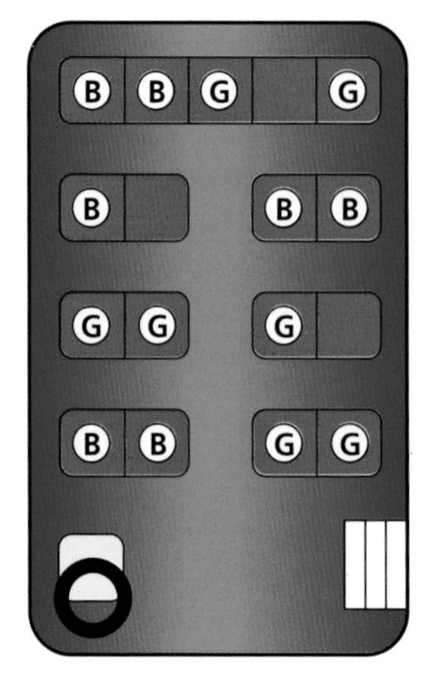

Using B for boy and G for girl, the distribution was as shown.

Equal Terms

Rating 2 Points

BILL = 13

TILL = 16

BITE = 23

BELT = 22

TILE = ?

Each letter represents a different number from 1 - 9
and they are added together to give the answer.
What is the sum of the letters in TILE?

Equal Terms - Solution

BILL = 13

TILL = 16

BITE = 23

BELT = 22

TILE = 19

19. From the last two equations I = L + 1.
Therefore B + 3L = 12 and the only value of
L to give valid values for I and B is 2.
This gives B = 6, I = 3, T = 9 and E = 5.

Codenames

Rating 3 Points

Clare and Simon have four children. When Simon is away working, Clare writes to him about the children, but she always uses a code for their names in case they read the letters. What are their names?

Codenames - Solution

1652 = LISA
0231 = CARL
5429 = SEAN
3854 = ROSE

C	L	A	R	E	S	I	M	O	N
0	1	2	3	4	5	6	7	8	9

All the children's names are made up from the letters CLARESIMON. Each letter is assigned a number from 0 - 9.

Frame Up

Rating 2 Points

Fit the tiles into the frame so that the edges of the tiles that touch the sides of the frame are the same colour as the frame.

Frame Up - Solution

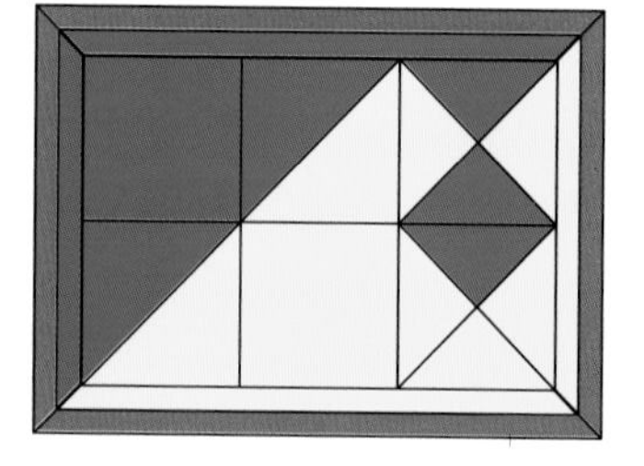

The only solution is as shown.

Champagne Surprise

Rating 1 Point

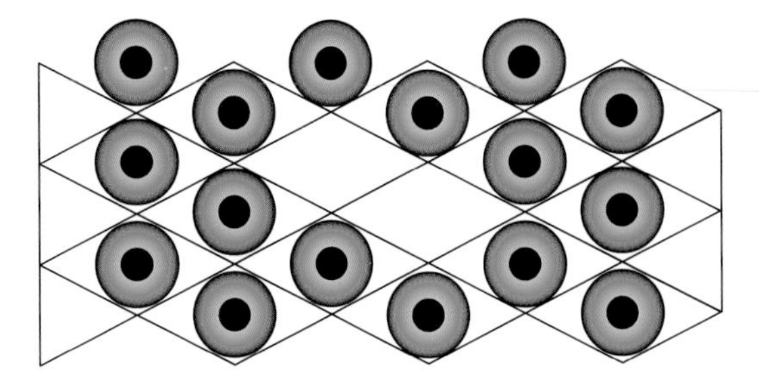

A wine rack contains 16 bottles as shown. There are five red, five rose and five white wines and a bottle of champagne. The top and bottom rows have a red, rose and white in that order. No column or row has more than one of any kind. There is more white and more rose in the top half than there is in the bottom half. The champagne lies between two whites. Where is it?

Champagne Surprise - Solution

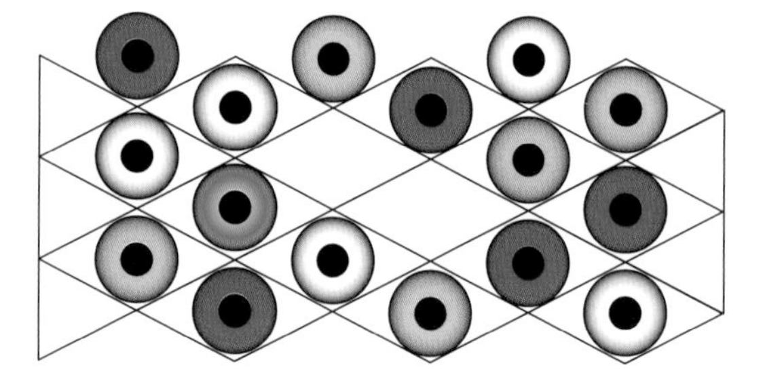

The bottle of champagne is the green bottle shown in the diagram.

Double Dealing

Rating 2 Points

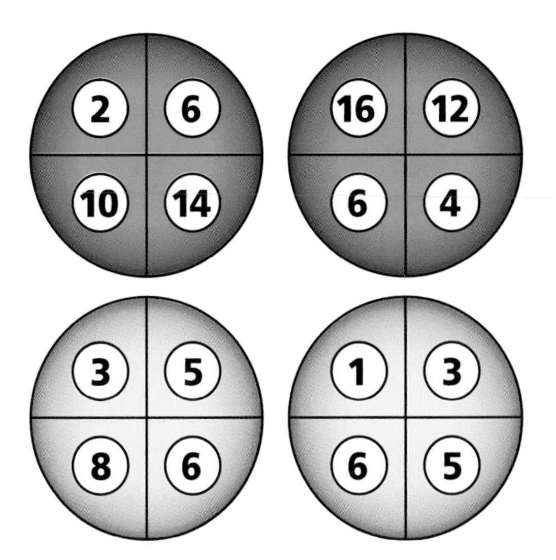

Two balls resting on a table are both split into 8 numbered segments and are shown seen from the front and the rear. Arrange the balls so that their front views give a total of 55.

Double Dealing - Solution

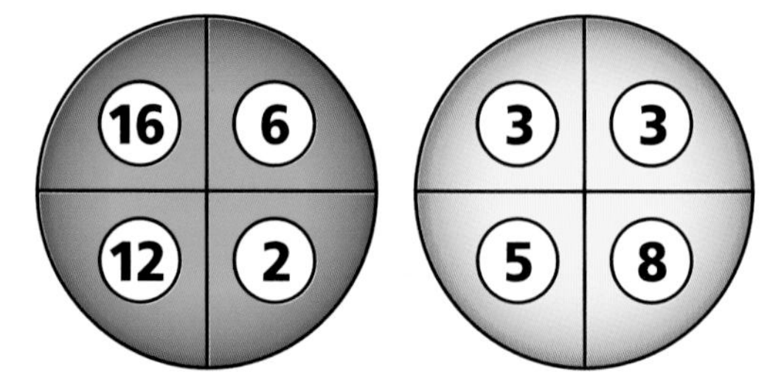

The only arrangement is as shown.

False Front

Rating 3 Points

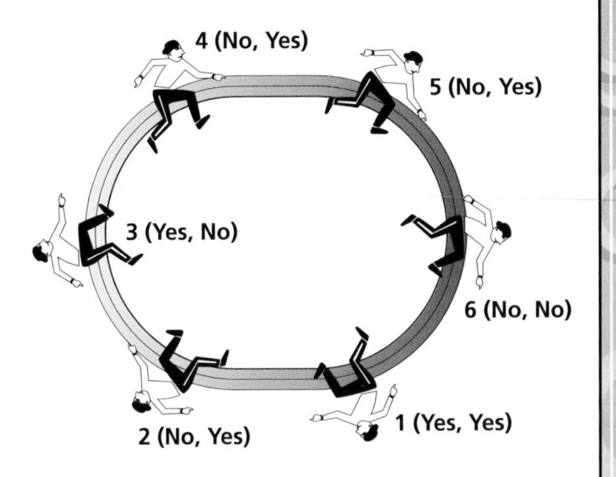

The six guards, three red and three blue, of Laguna are training for a relay race and as such have discarded their coloured tunics for white vests. Either all the red guards tell the truth and all the blue guards lie or vice versa. One of the guards holds the baton as they run round the track in a clockwise direction. They were all asked the two questions. *"Does the guard in front of you tell the truth and does the guard behind you hold the baton?"*. Their replies are shown. Which one holds the baton?

False Front - Solution

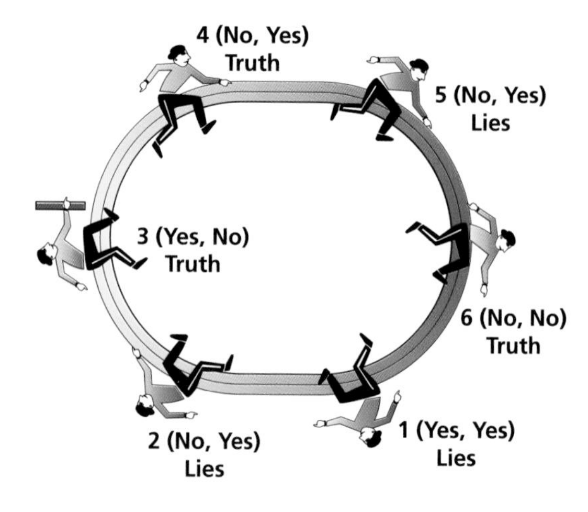

Guard number three holds the baton.
(Guards 1, 2 and 5 lied and
guards 3, 4 and 6 told the truth.)

F1 Quandary

Rating 2 Points

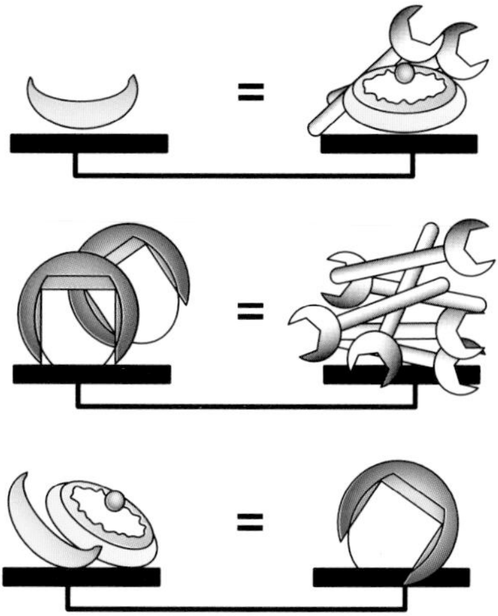

Alberto Paccanaro is about to start a Formula 1 race. He needs a snack, but he mustn´t increase his weight by too much. He knows one banana is allowed, but unfortunately he hates bananas. Using the information below, work out how many buns Alberto can have instead.

A Quandary - Solution

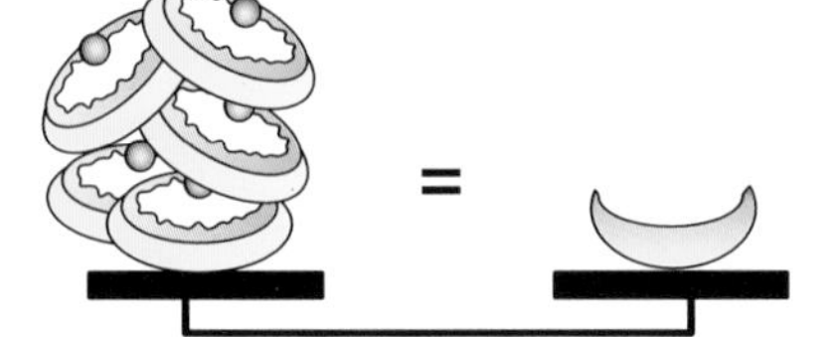

He could eat five buns.

Hoopla

Rating 3 Points

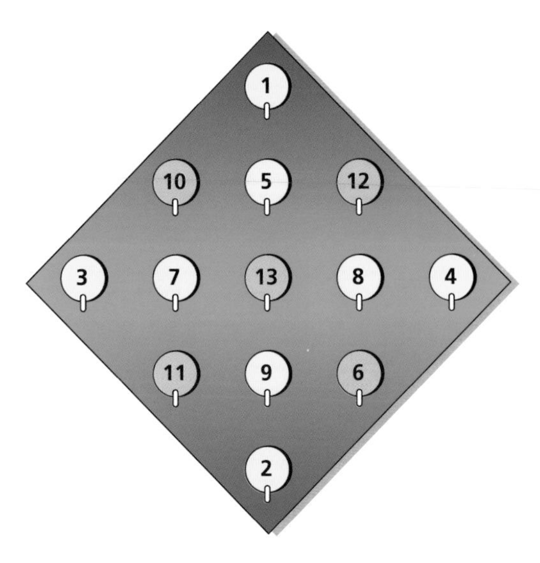

Five hoops were thrown at the board. One missed. None of the remaining four was in the same line, vertically or horizontally. The total scored was 29. What were the four different numbers that were hooped?

Hoopla - Solution

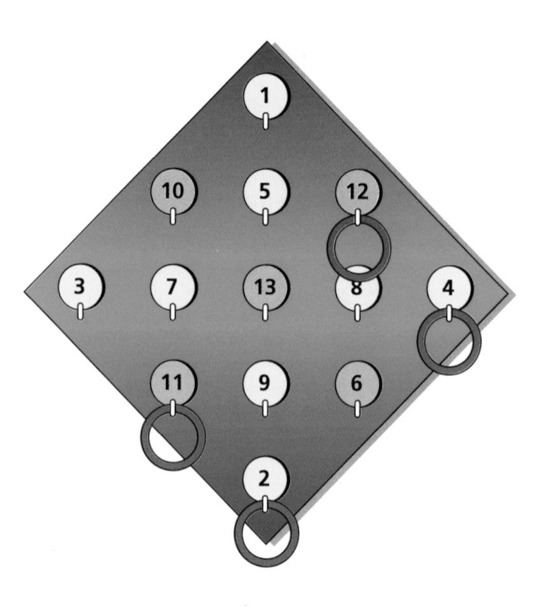

2, 4, 11 and 12.

Close Call

Rating 1 Point

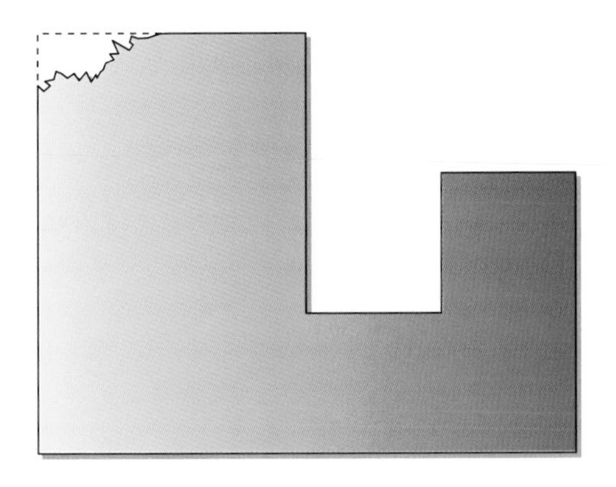

A manufacturer has an order to provide plastic pieces for a board game, where two identical shapes are required, with one approximately eight times larger than the other. On the first production run most of the larger shapes have a damaged edge as shown. Rather than destroy these items the manufacturer makes good use of them. How?

Close Call - Solution

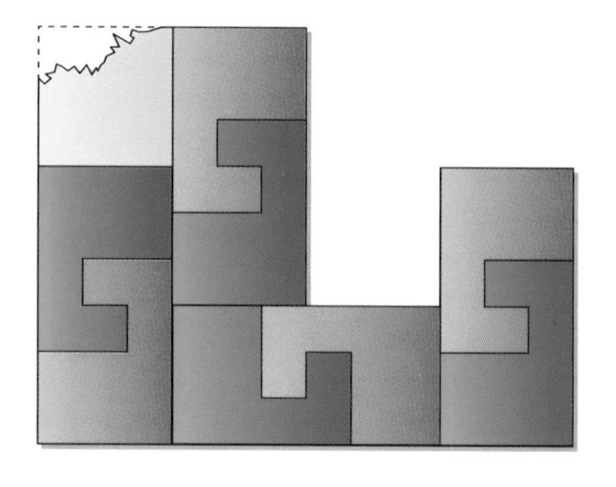

The manufacturer cuts them up
into eight identical shapes as shown.

Winning Numbers

Rating 2 Points

Lottery balls are numbered 1 - 9 white, 10 - 19 blue, 20 - 29 pink, 30 - 39 green, and 40 - 49 yellow. At a recent draw the six winning numbers were written down as they appeared: 14291342837. There was at least one ball of each colour. What were the numbers?

Winning Numbers - Solution

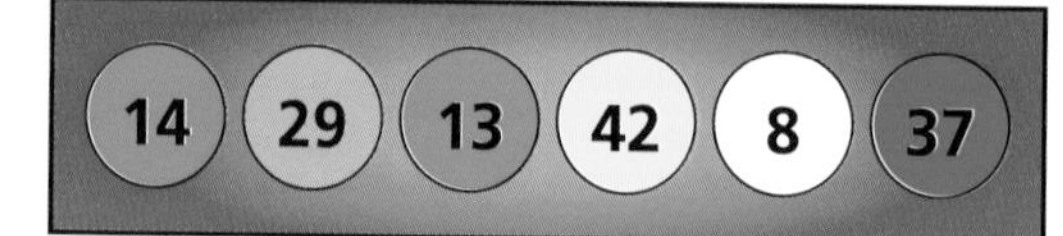

The numbers could only have been as shown.

Rating 3 Points

What encrypted well-known phrase is this, taken from Shakespeare's *Twelfth Night*?

Duke's Delight - Solution

I	F	M	U	S	I	C	B	E	T	H	E	F	O	O	D
1	2	3	4	1	2	3	4	1	2	3	4	1	2	3	4

O	F	L	O	V	E	P	L	A	Y	O	N
1	2	3	4	1	2	3	4	1	2	3	4

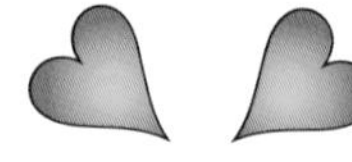

1	2	3	4	5	6	7	8	9
A	B	C	D	E	F	G	H	I
J	K	L	M	N	O	P	Q	R
S	T	U	V	W	X	Y	Z	

Number the letters in the coded phrase 1234, 1234 etc. Then, to decipher the meaning of the phrase, find the first letter in the table above and count back 1 letter to find that J = 1, similarly find the H then count back 2 letters to find H = F etc.

Cover Up

Rating 1 Point

What is the maximum number of postage stamps, size 3cm (1.18in) by 2cm (0.79in), that you can stick on one side of an envelope measuring 22.5cm (8.86in) by 13.5cm (5.31in), without any overlapping or stamps going over the edge?

Cover Up - Solution

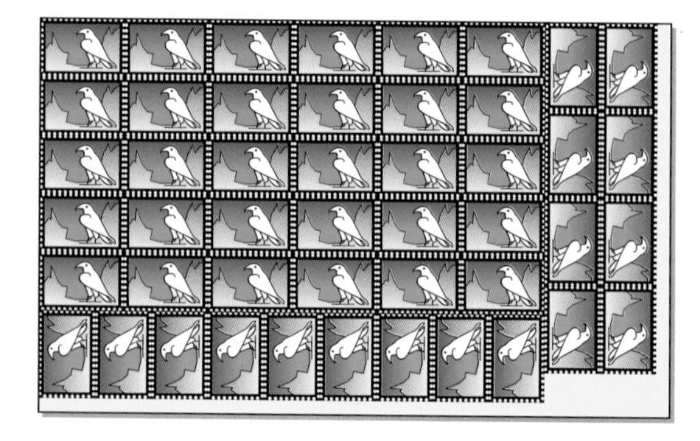

A block of five by six, plus a block of four by two,
plus a block of nine, which equals a total of 47 as shown.

Overall Scoring Page

CHAPTER	SCORE CARD	POTENTIAL SCORE	YOUR SCORE
1	Page 8	**40**	_____
2	Page 54	**40**	_____
3	Page 100	**45**	_____
4	Page 146	**45**	_____
		GRAND TOTAL	_____

Anyone who has scored more than 128 points can afford to sit back and feel smug – Well done you're in the top 25%

Anyone who got between 85 and 128 points should be content knowing they got more than half of these cryptic conundrums correct.

Those with less than 85 points, however, should turn over to page 192 for more information on Lagoon's other Brain-Boosting titles - you really should do a bit more practice!

OTHER TITLES AVAILABLE FROM LAGOON BOOKS:

BRAIN-BOOSTING PUZZLE BOOKS

BRAIN-BOOSTING VISUAL LOGIC PUZZLES
(ISBN: 1902813200)

BRAIN-BOOSTING LATERAL THINKING PUZZLES
(ISBN: 1902813227)

MIND-BENDING PUZZLE BOOKS

MIND-BENDING LATERAL THINKING PUZZLES
(ISBN 1899712062)

MORE MIND-BENDING LATERAL THINKING PUZZLES - VOLUME II
(ISBN 1899712194)

MIND-BENDING LATERAL THINKING PUZZLES BY DES MACHALE
(ISBN 1899712232)

MIND-BENDING CONUNDRUMS & PUZZLES
(ISBN 1899712038)

MIND-BENDING CLASSIC LOGIC PUZZLES
(ISBN 1899712186)

MIND-BENDING CLASSIC WORD PUZZLES
(ISBN 1899712054)

MIND-BENDING CROSSWORD PUZZLES
(ISBN 1899712399)

MIND-BENDING CHALLENGING LOGIC PUZZLES
(ISBN 1899712240)

MIND-BENDING CHALLENGING OPTICAL PUZZLES
(ISBN 1899712690)

MIND-BENDING MAZE PUZZLES
(ISBN 1899712720)